# The
# Sea
# Chart

# The Sea Chart

An Historical Survey
based on the Collections
in the
National Maritime Museum

*Derek Howse*
*and*
*Michael Sanderson*

With an Introduction by
Rear-Admiral G S Ritchie CB DSC
President of the
Directing Committee of the
International Hydrographic Bureau
Monaco
Former Hydrographer of the Navy

*McGraw - Hill Book Company*
*New York · Toronto · Mexico · Panama · Johannesburg*

Library of Congress Catalog Card Number: 72-11575
SBN: 07-030602-8

Set in 10/11 point Ehrhardt
and printed in Great Britain
by Fletcher & Son Ltd, Norwich, England

# Contents

|  | page |
|---|---|
| List of Charts | 7 |
| Introduction | 9 |
| Authors' Preface | 14 |
| General Bibliography and List of Abbreviations | 15 |
| Charts I–LX inclusive | 16 to 135 |
| Acknowledgements | 136 |
| National Maritime Museum Chart References | 137 |
| Index | 139 |

# List of Charts

| | | *page* |
|---|---|---|
| I | *Corfu* by Cristoforo Buondelmonte | 16 |
| II | *Mediterranean and North East Atlantic* by Jacobo Bertran and Berenguer Ripol | 18 |
| III | *Rhodes* by Bartolommeo dalli Sonetti | 20 |
| IV | *The World* by Francesco Rosselli | 22 |
| V | *North America—East Coast*, probably by Girolamo Verrazano | 24 |
| VI | *Atlantic Ocean*, probably by Pedro Reinel | 26 |
| VII | *Adriatic Sea and Eastern Mediterranean* by Giovanni Andrea di Vavassore | 28 |
| VIII | *The South Pacific* by Gerard Mercator | 30 |
| IX | *Pacific Ocean* by Battista Agnese | 32 |
| X | *Gulf of St Lawrence* by a Portuguese | 34 |
| XI | *Central Mediterranean* by Diogo Homem and Paolo Forlani | 36 |
| XII | *The Passage from England to the Gulf of Finland* by William Borough | 38 |
| XIII | *The Coast of Brittany* by Lucas Janszoon Waghenaer | 40 |
| XIV | *Baltic Sea. The Coast of Estonia and Bay of Tallinn* by L. J. Waghenaer and Anthony Ashley | 42 |
| XV | *Eastern Mediterranean and Black Sea* by Joan Oliva | 44 |
| XVI | *Bay of Biscay and English Channel* by Thomas Hood | 46 |
| XVII | *The South Coast of England between Portland and Dover* by Willem Janszoon Blaeu and Jan Jansson | 48 |
| XVIII | *South West Atlantic* by Antonio Sanches | 50 |
| XIX | *Western Mediterranean* by John Burston | 52 |
| XX | *The Pacific Coast of North West America* by Sir Robert Dudley | 54 |
| XXI | *The North Sea* by Jacob Aertsz Colom and Arnold Colom | 56 |
| XXII | *North Carolina, Pamlico and Albemarle Sounds* by Nicholas Comberford | 58 |

| | | |
|---|---|---|
| XXIII | *The East Indies* by Hendrick Doncker | 60 |
| XXIV | *The Pacific Ocean* by Pieter Goos | 62 |
| XXV | *England—East Coast* by John Seller | 64 |
| XXVI | *The Eastern Seaboard of North America* by John Seller | 66 |
| XXVII | *West Indies and Gulf of Mexico* by Joel Gascoyne | 68 |
| XXVIII | *The Azores (The Flemish Islands)* by Johannes van Keulen, the Elder | 70 |
| XXIX | *California* by Basil Ringrose | 72 |
| XXX | *Bombay* by John Thornton | 74 |
| XXXI | *The Scilly Islands* by Captain Greenvile Collins | 76 |
| XXXII | *Gironde Estuary and River* by Alexis Hubert Jaillot and Pierre Mortier | 78 |
| XXXIII | *The English Channel* after Edmond Halley | 80 |
| XXXIV | *The Gulf of Finland* by Alexei Nagaev | 82 |
| XXXV | *The Approaches to the Port of Amoy, Fukien* by Johannes van Keulen, the Younger | 84 |
| XXXVI | *The South China Sea* by William Herbert | 86 |
| XXXVII | *St Lawrence River—the Traverse* by James Cook | 88 |
| XXXVIII | *Western Mediterranean and the Strait of Gibraltar* by Joseph Roux | 90 |
| XXXIX | *Gibraltar Bay* by Jacques Nicolas Bellin | 92 |
| XL | *The Harbour of Port Royal, Jamaica* by Captain Joseph Speer | 94 |
| XLI | *Approaches to Canton* by Alexander Dalrymple | 96 |
| XLII | *New Zealand* by James Cook | 98 |
| XLIII | *Parts of the Coast of Brittany* by J. N. Bellin et al | 100 |
| XLIV | *Sumatra—West Coast* by Jean-Baptiste D'Après de Mannevillette | 102 |
| XLV | *Part of the Island of Lewis and the Minches* by Murdoch Mackenzie, Senior | 104 |
| XLVI | *Callao, Peru* by Luis de Surville | 106 |
| XLVII | *Sable Island, off Nova Scotia* by Joseph Frederick Wallet Des Barres | 108 |
| XLVIII | *Boston, Massachusetts* by Emeric Vidal | 110 |
| XLIX | *Plan of the Port of Santander, Spain* by Don Vicente Tofiño de San Miguel | 112 |
| L | *Torres Strait* by Matthew Flinders | 114 |
| LI | *Alexandria, Egypt* by British Admiralty | 116 |
| LII | *The Approaches to the Harbour of Brest, Brittany* by British Admiralty (Captain Thomas Hurd, RN) | 118 |
| LIII | *Taormina, Sicily* by British Admiralty (Captain, later Admiral, William Henry Smyth) | 120 |
| LIV | *The Solent and Spithead* by William Heather, revised by John William Norie | 122 |
| LV | *North Atlantic Ocean* by British Admiralty | 124 |
| LVI | *Coast of Peru* by James Imray & Son | 126 |
| LVII | *Arctic Coasts of Russia and Alaska* by US Hydrographic Office | 128 |
| LVIII | *Potomac River and Chesapeake Bay* by US Coast and Geodetic Survey | 130 |
| LIX | *Sound of Jura, Scotland, West Coast* by British Admiralty | 132 |
| LX | *English Channel to the Strait of Gibraltar* by British Admiralty | 134 |

8

# Introduction

Man used maps for finding his way many centuries before Christ, the earliest known map dating from the seventh or sixth century BC. It was a moulded clay tablet, and depicted the world as a flat disk, with Babylon in the centre surrounded by a mighty river named by Homer 'Okeanus'.

Both Pythagoras and Aristotle had shown by the fourth century BC that the earth was a globe, and Eratosthenes, keeper of the great library in Alexandria, accepting this, set out to measure the earth's circumference. His method was simple. Using existing field surveys of the fertile lands of the Nile Valley, he took the distance from Syene (modern Aswan) to Alexandria as 5,000 stadia (a stadium was about 200 yd). Syene lay on the Tropic of Cancer and Eratosthenes noticed that there was no shadow from a gnomon at the time of the summer solstice, whereas a similar gnomon at Alexandria threw a considerable shadow—whose length enabled him to calculate the angle subtended at the earth's centre between Syene and Alexandria as $7°$ $12'$, or $\frac{1}{50}$ of $360°$. Thus Eratosthenes could assess the earth's circumference as 252,000 stadia, just 4 per cent in excess of modern calculations, which surely makes him the founder of geodesy.

About 100 AD a man, or it could have been an organisation, known as Marinus of Tyre began drawing maps for the use of seamen based on a cylindrical projection forming a grid of parallelograms centred on Rhodes, the marine focal point of the known world. It is only through the writings of one of the greatest geographers of all time that we know what we do of Marinus, for Ptolemy consciously built upon the former's work. Ptolemy was an astronomer and mathematician living in Alexandria in the second century AD. He wrote a great deal, his best known work being *Geographia*, in which he discusses geodesy and the mathematics of cartography, and lists the latitude and longitude co-ordinates of 8,000 places, culled from ancient maps or estimated from a study of traveller's tales.

Ptolemy, believing that the known world occupied half the circuit of the globe, numbered his meridians 0°–180° from west to east, starting from the Fortunate Islands (Canaries), the furthest land then reported to the west. In *Geographia* he discusses three projection systems which he had devised for representing the sphere, or at least half of it, on a flat surface, the simplest being his conic projection, which he described thus:

> What must be done should one desire to delineate the earth on a plane surface. Wherefore we shall do well to keep straight lines for our meridians, but to insert our parallels as the arcs of circles, having one and the same centre, which we suppose to be the North Pole, and from which we draw straight lines of our meridians, keeping above all else similarity to a sphere, in the form and appearance of our plane surface.

Ptolemy's world map drawn on his second projection shows the Mediterranean with some accuracy. It indicates the existence of England and Scotland, and even Iceland, but Africa appears as a vast continent continuing across the southern Indian Ocean and then northwards to join China. The Indian sub-continent is shown and the island of Ceylon, though their relative sizes are almost reversed; but the Red Sea and the Persian Gulf are fairly accurately depicted.

The Romans' interest in cartography was largely restricted to route maps, drawn on long narrow scrolls, for use along the great military roads crossing the empire. Ptolemy's *Geographia*, together with his maps and his projections, were to remain neglected through the long dark ages of cartography.

From the earliest times direction at sea in the Mediterranean had been identified by the prevailing winds from eight equally spaced directions around the horizon; 'Tramontana' from the north, 'Levante' from the east, and 'Syroco' from the southeast being but three of these named directions, or 'rhumbs' as they were termed, along which crude courses could be steered before the following wind.

When, and by whom, the properties of the lodestone and the magnetic needle were first discovered is far from clear. The early use of the compass at sea has frequently been described in literature: one instance, cited by the late Professor Taylor in her *Haven Finding Art*, quotes Jacques de Vitry, a Bishop of Acre, who wrote as follows in 1218:

> An iron needle after it has made contact with the magnet stone, always turns towards the North Star, which stands motionless while the rest revolve, being as it were the axis of the firmament. It is therefore a necessity for those travelling by sea.

The magnetic compass gradually evolved from a needle floating in a bowl of water into a system of thin magnetised metal rods secured beneath a pivoted circular card on which was painted the wind rose with its eight rhumbs, and later their halves and quarters, making thirty-two points in all. The radiating rhumbs were drawn in tapered form, so that the whole design had a starlike appearance—because it was to the seaman's guiding star, or the Christian Stella Maris, that the north point of the compass was ever, almost magically, directed. Installed in a box for safekeeping, with a light nearby to aid the steersman at night, the compass was in common use by Mediterranean seamen during the mid-thirteenth century.

Towards the end of this century references may be found to the use of charts in Mediterranean vessels. In the next century appeared the workmanlike 'portulan charts', the first of them drawn on vellum in Venice and Genoa, the leading maritime states of the day. The word *portolano* had been used for some time to refer to an earlier form of written pilot or seaman's guide, and thus 'portulan chart' has been used by cartographic historians to differentiate between the written guides and the drawn charts; these latter are also sometimes called 'compass charts', for the concept of the compass has been set down upon a plane chart, owing nothing to Ptolemy's still lost ideas for depicting a sphere on a flat surface.

An interesting step between the *portolano* and the portulan chart is the Italian *isolaria*, or island guide, which includes written, and sometimes poetic, directions for navigation, together with crudely drawn coastlines of the islands lying on the route between Italy and Constantinople.

To make a portulan chart the cartographer first set down on his prepared sheepskin or goatskin a number of compass stars from which he extended the rhumb lines to cover the whole area. These enabled him to draw in the coastlines and remained as a network of bearings from which the navigator pricked off his courses with a pair of compasses (dividers) and a ruler.

Little hinterland detail is shown on the portulan chart, the land area being used for the insertion of copious names, the flags and banners of the coastal states, and vignettes of cities and seaports. The easterly magnetic variation of about 11°, which was then unknown, accounts for the inclination of the eastern end of the Mediterranean towards the north on most portulan charts.

During the thirteenth century the kingdom of Aragon, which included the ports of Palma, Barcelona, and Valencia, as well as those in Sicily, became an important maritime state. Charts were now necessities and a centre of Catalan cartography developed at Palma, which, though relying at first on Italian cartographers, eventually prepared its portulan charts with a distinct Catalan style, including scales of 'portulan miles', which approximate to the Catalan league of about 6,000 metres.

In the fourteenth century it was the turn of Portugal to expand her maritime trade, vessels from Lisbon and Oporto sailing increasingly to southern England and Flanders for cargoes of wool. In 1385 Portugal's neighbouring state, Castille, attacked her, only to be defeated decisively on the historic battleground of Aljubarrota. English bowmen assisted the Portuguese to win their victory and, in the following year, the long-lasting alliance between England and Portugal was formed, and King João I married John of Gaunt's daughter Philippa.

This couple had four talented sons, the third of whom, Henriques, was to gain fame as Henry the Navigator. As a young man he took a prominent part in the expedition that captured Ceuta in 1415, and thereafter he devoted his life to fostering the exploration of the Atlantic Coast of Africa. He established his residence near the Sagres peninsula in southern Portugal, and there attracted around him cosmographers and cartographers to study and develop methods of ocean navigation, and to prepare to record the national discoveries Henry expected to be made far across the sea.

Among those who came to Sagres was Jafuda Cresques, son of the Jewish leader of the Catalan school of cartographers, anxious to escape the increasing persecution of the Jews in Aragon. He brought with him the established skills of chart-drawing, which he passed on to Henry's Portuguese cartographers.

Henry died in 1460 at a time when his caravels were sailing as far south as the coast of Guinea and his explorers were sailing up the Gambia and other African rivers in search of the fabled Christian kingdom of Prester John. It was twenty-eight years before Bartolemeu Dias discovered and rounded the Cape of Good Hope, and another ten before Vasco da Gama reached India in 1498. In 1500 Cabral, sailing to extend da Gama's explorations in the east, was set so far to the westward in the Atlantic on his voyage to the Cape that he sighted the coast of Brazil, which, as it lay to the east of the demarcation line between Spanish and Portuguese territories established at the Treaty of Tordesillas in 1494, he claimed for Portugal. Henry the Navigator had never sailed on the Portuguese voyages, but he had sent numerous explorers on their way well prepared for the great new navigational problems involved.

Absorbed as they were in their route to the east, the king of Portugal and his advisers were not interested in a proposal by a young Genoese named Columbus to rediscover Marco Polo's Cipangu (Japan) by sailing westwards across the Atlantic, so he sought backing from the Spanish Court and discovered the New World in 1493. The Portuguese, however, had made sufficient discoveries of their own to keep their cartographers busy. Although very few of their fifteenth-century charts survive, there remains a great deal of beautiful work from the first half of the sixteenth century. The most famous of the Portuguese cartographers were probably Pedro and Jorge Reinel. The latter once temporarily abandoned his homeland after a street brawl to work in Seville for Magellan, who was preparing for the voyage that was to encircle the globe.

In the latter half of the fifteenth century the Portuguese cosmographers had provided their seamen with the quadrant for observing the altitude of the Pole Star, and later of the sun, to find latitude. By the 1480s tables of the sun's declination and a *Regiment of the North*, which gave corrections to be made to Pole Star observations according to the position of the adjacent stars known as the 'Guards', were also made available to the Portuguese navigator. Thus 'running down the latitude' became the accepted form of navigation when making a landfall after an ocean passage, a method reflected on the charts by the introduction about 1500 of latitude scales, which with 70 miles to a degree show that Eratosthenes' figure for the earth's circumference had survived the Dark Ages.

Sometime, after the return of Vasco da Gama from India, Portugal established the Casa da India in Lisbon to administer the trade to Africa and India; in addition up-to-date charts were maintained and ocean pilots were examined. In 1504 Spain had established the Casa de Contratacion in Seville for a similar purpose, so that perhaps Portugal and Spain must be given the distinction of providing the world's first hydrographic offices.

In 1530 the King of Portugal appointed Pedro Nunes, a skilled cosmographer, to be Hidrof-mor (chief hydrographer) at the Casa da India, and Portuguese navigators drew the attention of Nunes to the difficulty they experienced in steering ocean courses on a plane chart, which led him to study the problem. In 1537 he published his conclusions, which show that he realised that meridians converged towards the poles, and that, except at the equator, a course crossing the meridians at a constant angle is not a great circle but a spiral rhumb line.

An extremely important event in world cartography had taken place in 1400 when Palla-Strozzi, a Florentine patron of letters, obtained in Constantinople a manuscript of Ptolemy's *Geo-*

*graphia*, together with the associated maps and treatises on mapmaking that had been lost to the world for over 1,000 years. The work was translated into Latin from the ancient Greek of the manuscript, and leading cosmographers and geographers began to arrive in Florence to make copies and translations into their respective languages.

By the mid-fifteenth century printing and reproduction from copper and wood engraving had arrived and, from 1477, editions of *Geographia*, often brought up-to-date by the inclusion of detail from the latest maps, began slowly to spread outwards from the Italian presses to the civilised world, taking with them Ptolemy's ideas of how the spherical Earth could be represented on a flat surface.

Thus, from the end of the fifteenth century, Italian, Portuguese, and Spanish cartographers, becoming increasingly aware of the land masses of the world as Ptolemy showed them, of the latitude and longitude grid system and of Ptolemy's projections, tried to fit into the Ptolemaic framework the new discoveries of Columbus and Vespucci, John Cabot and the Cortereal brothers, Vasco da Gama and Cabral, and many others. This was an exciting period for world cartography, made more so by the rapid development of printing and engraving techniques, which made possible the publication of 'atlases', as collections of maps or charts were named after the depiction of Atlas carrying the world on his shoulders on the title page of one of the earliest of these collections prepared by Lafreri in Italy.

The focus of mapmaking and chartmaking now began to move northwards to the Netherlands where, in Antwerp in 1570, Ortelius published his atlas *Theatrum Orbis Terrarum*, which, among many others, contained a significant world map. Using the prime meridian through the Canary Islands, the world is drawn on a projection developed from that of Ptolemy, but showing the full 180° both to the west and to the east of the prime meridian. The new discoveries are shown with the Pacific rightly placed to the west of a rather 'fat' South America. A vast continent encircling the southern portion of the world and named 'Australis Nondum Cognita' is, however, all that is left of the land masses as Ptolemy saw them.

More significant from the mariner's point of view, though it was not realised widely at the time, was the publication by Gerard Mercator of his 'world chart of 1569' in eighteen sheets. Mercator was described by his friend Ortelius as 'the greatest geographer since Ptolemy', and seamen will not quarrel with this.

Mercator devised for his world chart a latitude and longitude grid system that elegantly solved the problem of steering rhumb-line courses, which Nunes had puzzled over in Portugal thirty years earlier. Mercator's 'projection', as it is now universally termed by navigators, depends on the principle that the convergence of meridians is in proportion to the cosine of the latitude. If a proportional misplacement is introduced into the spacing between the parallels of latitude on the chart as they move away from the equator, then spiral rhumb lines cutting each meridian at the same angle become straight lines.

Although Mercator's method of constructing a chart was tailormade for the seaman, it took nearly another century before most of them abandoned their awkward but familiar plane charts. It was an Englishman, Edward Wright, Fellow of Cambridge, who in his *Certaine Errors of Navigation*, published in 1599, made clear to the sailor the benefits to be gained by adopting Mercator's method. He described it in terms of a bladder

blown up inside a cylinder and went on to show in simple terms how rhumb lines could be drawn as straight lines on a chart compiled on Mercator's principle. A printed chart of the NE Atlantic constructed in this way, and included in *Certaine Errors*, marks a revolution in the design of sea charts.

Following the success of Ortelius' atlas, the Netherlands took the lead in publishing sea charts, a novelty for northern European mariners, who had traditionally navigated by lead and line, relying on pilot books or rutters for the courses required to reach one cape from another—'caping' as they called it. They laughed when they met Mediterranean sailors with their 'sheepskins'.

In the Netherlands, as elsewhere, it was the *leeskart* (reading chart) that developed first and it was not until the mid-sixteenth century that Cornelius Anthonisz, who had been associated with 'leeskarten', published the first *paskart* (passage chart) of the East Sea (Baltic). He was followed by an increasing number of Dutch chartmakers until a significant stage was reached in 1584 with the publication of Lucas Janszoon Waghenaer's sea-atlas *Spieghel der Zeevaert*. This work, in two parts, was an extensive bound collection of engraved charts, together with written sailing directions, for navigation from the Baltic to Cadiz.

Still owing much to the Mediterranean portulan chart in the way that compasses and rhumb lines were set down, these charts were designed by a sea pilot of long experience. Soundings reduced to a half-tide datum were shown for anchorages and harbour bars; topography was drawn in panoramic style as seen from seaward, and views were included to assist coastal identification. Much of the coastal detail was probably plotted by intersecting compass bearings taken from a ship at different positions as she ran along the coast while paying close attention to her log.

Except on one small scale chart covering the whole area from North Cape to the Canaries, no latitude or longitude scales are shown. Scales of Dutch miles of 15 to the degree and Spanish miles of $17\frac{1}{2}$ to the degree are placed conspicuously in a 'box' on each chart. Standard symbols were introduced for the first time to show safe anchorages, buoys, and submerged rocks.

The Netherlands ambassador showed a copy of *Spieghel der Zeevaert* to England's Lord High Admiral, Lord Howard, who arranged for a translation and publication in England. As *The Mariners' Mirrour* it made its appearance in 1588, the year of the Armada, and its success was such that British seamen referred to every similar collection of charts as 'waggoners' for a century to come.

Blaeu followed Waghenaer with his own atlas *Het Licht de Seevaert* of 1608, which was also translated into English. Blaeu took greater pains than his predecessor to publish new editions in order to keep his work up-to-date.

It was not until the 1670s that an English cartographer named Seller tried to break the Dutch monopoly by publishing an atlas in England, but he owed everything to the Netherlands chartmakers, even to the extent of buying their old copper plates and re-engraving portions of them in London to give them a convincing appearance.

It was clear that the Dutch knew more about the English coasts than the British seamen did themselves, and after nearly 100 years' reliance upon the Dutch chartmakers Samuel Pepys, Secretary of the Navy, issued an Admiralty order in June 1681 assigning a naval officer, Captain Greenvile Collins, to the task of surveying the British coasts and harbours. Even with two yachts provided, Collins had an enormous task, for there was at that time no national triangulation in existence on which he could base his work. With a measuring chain, a compass, a leadline and little else he took seven years to complete the work that was published as *Great Britain's Coasting Pilot* in 1693; it contained forty-eight harbour and coastal charts.

These were still plane charts, similar in many ways to those of Waghenaer and Blaeu, with well-executed views illustrating leading and clearing lines along which ships could safely sail to enter harbour. Much criticised in official circles and compared unfavourably with *The New Large Shining Sea-Torch*, published by the house of Van Keulen in Amsterdam four years previously, and *Le Neptune François* published by order of Louis XIV in the same year, *Great Britain's Coasting Pilot* still met the needs of British seamen and ran into at least a dozen editions during the eighteenth century. Volumes of this atlas still come to light, often heavily annotated by individual sea captains, who obviously set much store by their own English 'waggoner'.

In the late seventeenth century, under Le Roi Soleil and his sea-minded Secretary of State Colbert, France enjoyed a scientific awakening. Among other advances was the establishment in 1667 of L'Observatoire de Paris, whose purpose was to bring about a better understanding of the celestial sphere and to improve maps and charts. An Italian cosmographer named Cassini, whose son and grandsons also worked for France, became the virtual director of L'Observatoire in 1669, having finally made practicable Galileo's method of finding longitude on land by the observation of Jupiter's satellites. Once the latitude and longitude of Paris had been established a triangulated survey of the whole of France was put in hand. Many coastal positions were fixed in relation to the meridian of Paris, allowing the whole coastline to be redrawn by 1681, though the resultant shrinking of France's boundaries is said not to have been well received by the king.

It is not surprising that the charts in *Le Neptune François*, therefore, based as they were on the new national survey, were superior to those of Greenvile Collins, who had set down his coastline with a measuring chain unrelated to any national framework. The French charts were constructed by the Mercator method, and their advantage to seamen is clearly described in the foreword to *Le Neptune François*.

Le Dépôt des Cartes et Plans de la Marine was established in 1720 and through this office further editions of *Le Neptune François* and other atlases were published during the eighteenth century under the direction of J. N. Bellin, whose impeccable standards are clearly recognisable. His finest work is perhaps *Le Petit Atlas Maritime* of 1764, whose clean, clear cut style is reflected in the engraving of the coastline, topography and highly legible lettering.

Although longitude observations were now possible ashore, at sea the problem was still intractable. Charles II had founded the Royal Observatory at Greenwich for the study of nautical astronomy, as it was believed the solution would be found in the skies; and in 1714 the British Parliament passed the Longitude Act, which provided a vast financial reward to 'such person or persons who shall discover longitude at sea'. While succeeding Astronomers Royal searched for a celestial solution, others were convinced that a seagoing clock would solve the question.

The long history of how John Harrison constructed his four timepieces (all now in daily going order at the National Maritime Museum, Greenwich), and of his struggle to obtain the £20,000 reward at the age of seventy-eight, is a story in itself. Harrison's no 4, with which finally he won the prize, is a most elegant timepiece; it had to be dismantled in the presence of six clockmakers so that they would know how to make similar watches commercially. Captain Cook carried such a copy, Kendall's no 1, on his second voyage to the Pacific in 1772, and he testified to its almost faultless timekeeping at sea, thus truly solving the longitude question.

By the mid-eighteenth century the use of a measured baseline and a network of triangles to establish interrelated positions had spread from the Continent. This system was employed by Murdoch Mackenzie in the Orkneys as the basis for the extension of a sounding survey within sight of the shore positions marked by beacons; and his *Orcades* is an atlas containing the results of the first of these systematic surveys, which he continued for another twenty years, with the backing of the Admiralty, down the west coast of Scotland and Wales and around the coasts of Ireland.

In retirement in 1770 Mackenzie published his *Treatise on Maritim Surveying*, in which he set down how the Hadley quadrant could be used for observing horizontal angles between three triangulated marks ashore, and how an instrument, subsequently to be named the 'station pointer', could be used to plot rapidly positions given by the two horizontal angles. The Hadley, developed in the early part of the eighteenth century by a vice-president of the Royal Society of that name, was an improved quadrant using reflecting mirrors that had superseded all other instruments used for measuring celestial altitudes at sea by the end of the eighteenth century.

For the next fifteen years Murdoch Mackenzie's nephew of the same name, assisted by Graeme Spence, carried out surveys for the Admiralty using the method of 'station pointer fixing' to locate the boat from which they were taking soundings with the leadline. This simple system revolutionised sea surveying and was universally adopted, the ever-increasing density of soundings on nineteenth-century charts testifying to its efficacy.

Britain began to play a leading role in chartmaking in the late eighteenth century. In the 1770s Des Barres, a Swiss serving with the British Army in North America, was supervising a number of surveyors working along the east Atlantic coast, and the results of these surveys were published in *Atlantic Neptune*, a superb series, destined to serve as the primary source for most north American charts for fifty years after the birth of the United States in 1783. Des Barres' published work reflects the high quality of copper engraving then being reached in England. *Atlantic Neptune* also showed a significant advance on previous atlases by including a sheet showing the many conventional symbols used in the 158 charts forming the collection.

In 1795 the Admiralty followed the example of the East India Company, appointing the Company's hydrographer, Alexander Dalrymple, to the same post in the Royal Navy. His first task was to make an inventory of all material available in London so that suitable charts could be compiled and produced for the use of the Fleet.

Charting around 1800 began to show a true picture of the world. Cook had disproved the existence of a great southern continent and placed New Zealand on the map; Flinders was laying down the coastline of Australia; Vancouver and Broughton carried on where Cook had left off, defining the limits of the north Pacific, to which La Perouse had further added before the loss of his ships; D'Entrecasteaux, searching for La Perouse, had also improved the charts of the south-west Pacific. The wealth of knowledge gained secretly by the Dutch in the East Indies in the seventeenth century was in addition now gradually becoming available.

The first printed Admiralty chart was issued early in the nineteenth century, but further charts did not come off the printing press in the Admiralty building quickly enough for the Royal Navy, engaged as it was in the Napoleonic wars at sea. Consequently in 1808 a naval captain, Hurd, who had a great deal of experience of sea surveying, was appointed to relieve Dalrymple, and he speeded up the supply of Admiralty charts to the Fleet. In 1823 these charts were first made available to merchantmen.

The nineteenth-century charts are characterised by the use of subdivided latitude and longitude borders, an increasing density of soundings and details concerning the nature of the sea bed, the insertion of parallels of latitude and meridians at well spaced intervals and the disappearance of rhumb lines emanating from compass roses. Simpler compass roses showing both true and magnetic circles began to appear, and a parallel ruler could be used to set down a course.

Admiralty surveying and charting probably reached its peak in the early 1850s at the end of Admiral Beaufort's long reign as Hydrographer. The charts of the period may be admired for their extensive world cover, their accuracy and their fine engraving, and those sold to the merchant fleet by London's chart-sellers in the nineteenth century must not be overlooked.

The United States formed a 'Survey of Coasts' in 1809, but apart from sending Hassler, its Swiss director, to Europe to study techniques and obtain instruments, little happened until 1830 when the Board of Commissioners for the Navy took the now traditional first step towards a hydrographic office by establishing a 'Depot of Charts and Instruments'. Sea-charting development in the United States, however, was to be unique among nations, for in 1832 Congress reactivated the Coast Survey and three years later, when it had acquired a copper printing press and the Navy a lithographic press, there were two charting agencies in the United States. During the Civil War (1861–5) many surveyors and draughtsmen were brought in from Europe and by the war's end the Coast Survey had made great advances in the standardisation of symbols and in colour printing. In 1866 the Naval Hydrographic Office was established in the Octagon Building in Washington and photolithography was introduced.

Although the existence of two agencies caused some inter-departmental bickering, it seems to have given impetus to innovations that made US charts superior to European, particularly in colour printing. The Coast Survey, which became the Coast and Geodetic Survey, was increasingly responsible for the geodetic triangulation ashore and the publishing of charts of home waters; while the US Hydrographic Office extended its activities worldwide.

Perhaps it was also because of these two national agencies that US cartographers became conscious of the need for standardisation of symbols, type-styles, borders and topography representation, a conviction they voiced in the international field. The prime mover in standardisation was, however, Ingénieur Hydrographe Renaud, in charge of the French Hydrographic Office, who, thwarted for a time by World War I, was able to persuade Rear-Admiral Sir John Parry, Britain's wartime hydrographer, to arrange the first International Hydrographic Conference, in London in 1919, which was attended by delegates from twenty-four states.

Parry, Renaud, and Captain Simpson, the US Naval Hydrographer, were nominated by the conference to take steps to establish a permanent international hydrographic bureau, which in fact began operating in Monaco, at the invitation of Prince Albert I, in 1921.

The Bureau has achieved a great deal over the last fifty years, particularly in the field of standardisation, as membership has increased to over forty. Students of marine cartography recognise the gradual move towards similarity, the best ideas of one nation being accepted by others on the recommendation of the Bureau.

By the end of the nineteenth century most European nations had abandoned *brasses* or *brazzas*, the measure of both arms outstretched, for depth measurements, in favour of the more precise metric system. Britain and the Commonwealth nations continued to use the fathom, or 6 ft, depth measurement until recently, when, accepting a long-standing Bureau recommendation, they decided to go over to the metric system. The US Oceanographic Office (formerly Hydrographic Office) is also adopting the metric system for showing depths on some of its overseas charts.

This significant step means that a great majority of the world's charts will shortly show depths in the same measurement, and the way ahead is open for the production of true international charts, at least on the smaller scales covering the oceans and seas. Only one nation will compile each chart, though other member states of the International Hydrographic Organisation may receive reproduction material from which to make their own copies of the original.

The final illustration in this book (Chart LX) is a new metric Admiralty chart, conforming in every way to the specifications laid down by the International Hydrographic Bureau for an international chart. The components, the styles, the structure, and the symbolisation which the Bureau has recommended for these charts have been developed over 500 years by many nations, taking the reader back to the Catalan portulan chart of 1456 (Chart II) with which it may be compared.

These two charts have one thing in common—both were compiled, designed, and produced with the best data and equipment available at the time to meet the needs of the contemporary mariner.

Department of Oceanography,            G. S. Ritchie
The University of Southampton        Rear-Admiral
May 1972

# Authors' Preface

The sixty reproductions which follow are all of sea charts preserved in the National Maritime Museum, Greenwich. Chosen primarily to illustrate the development of the sea chart during the period covered—1420 to the present day—they include charts of every part of the world, constructed on large and small scales, in manuscript and in printed form, the elegant and the not so elegant.

The bulk of the Museum's superb collection of maps and charts was assembled between 1930 and 1939, largely as a result of the munificence of the late Sir James Caird, Bt. They include not only the sea charts in sheet and atlas form, examples of which are illustrated in this book, but also a very important collection of general atlases including, for example, thirty-one different editions of Ptolemy's *Cosmographia* or *Geographica*, and three sets of Blaeu's celebrated *Atlas Maior*, two in Latin and one in French.

The general bibliography which follows includes only those books which deal with the history of sea charts or cartography generally. Specific references to individual charts or to their authors will be found on the page facing the reproduction of the chart concerned.

Robinson | Robinson, A. H. W. *Marine Cartography in Britain—A History of the Sea Chart to 1855* (Leicester, 1962)

Skelton (1958) | Skelton, R. A. *Explorers' Maps—Chapters in the Cartographic Record of Geographical Discovery* (1958)

Smith (1969) | Smith, T. R. 'Nicholas Comberford and the "Thames School" sea-chart makers of seventeenth-century London'. Unpublished paper read in Brussels 1969, summarised in *IM*, xxiv, 95

Waters (1958) | Waters, D. W. *The Art of Navigation in England in Elizabethan and Early Stuart Times* (1958)

# *General Bibliography and List of Abbreviations*

Bagrow-Skelton | Bagrow, L. & Skelton, R. A. *History of Cartography* (1964)

Cumming, Skelton & Quinn | Cumming, W. P., Skelton, R. A. & Quinn, D. B. *The Discovery of North America* (1971)

Dawson | Dawson, L. S. *Memoirs of Hydrography including Brief Biographies of the Principal Officers who have served in HM Surveying Service between the years 1750 and 1885* (Eastbourne, 1885, reprinted 1968)

Day | Day, Vice-Admiral Sir Archibald. *The Admiralty Hydrographic Service 1795–1919* (1967)

*HPC* | Cortesão, A. *History of Portuguese Cartography*, 2 vols (Coimbra, 1969 and 1971)

*IM* | *Imago Mundi: A Review of Early Cartography* (annual volumes)

Koeman | Koeman, C. *Atlantes Neerlandici*, 5 vols (Amsterdam, 1969–71)

*NMM Cat iii* | National Maritime Museum. *Catalogue of the Library, Vol iii, Atlases and Cartography*, 2 vols (1971)

*Periplus* | Nordenskiöld, A. E. *Periplus* (Stockholm, 1887)

*PMC* | Cortesão, A. & Teixeira da Mota, A. (eds). *Portugaliae Monumenta Cartographica*, 6 vols (Lisbon, 1960)

Ritchie | Ritchie, G. S. *The Admiralty Chart—British Naval Hydrography in the Nineteenth Century* (1967)

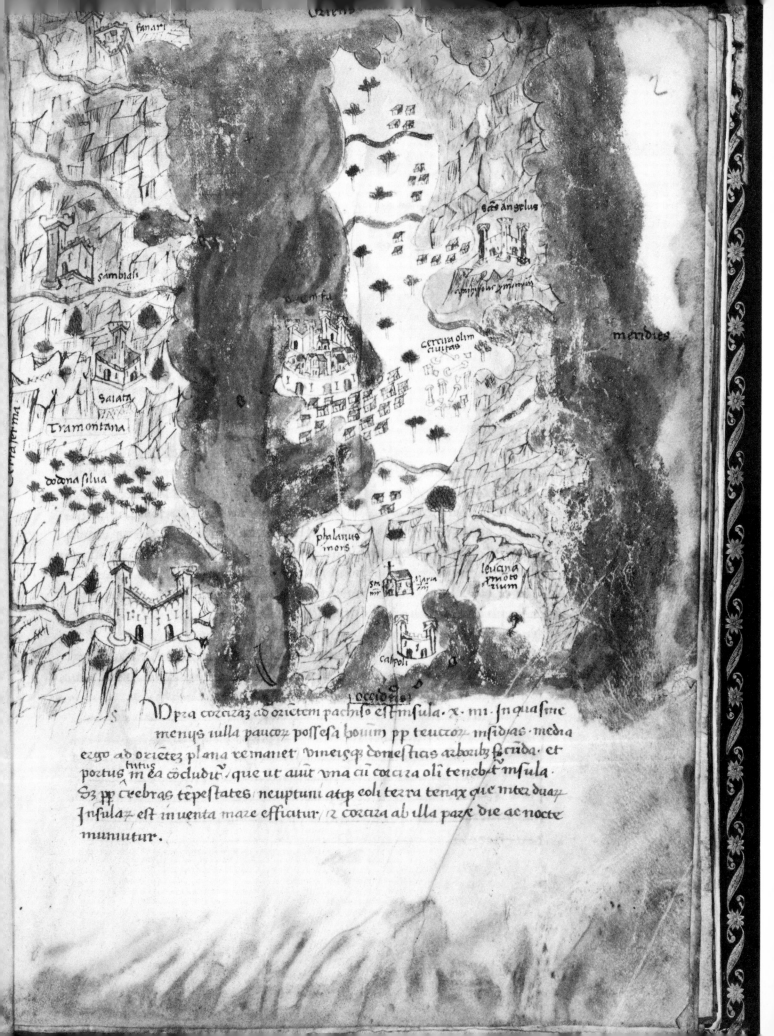

fanari

sãs ãngrlus

sambials

meridies

Salata

Tramontana

cerċia olim ċuitas

dodona silua

phalarius mors

leucana promontorium

cahpoli

occidens

Vḷtra coraczaz ad orietem pachīo est īsula. x. m̄. ī qua sme
menijs uilla paucoꝝ possesa bouū ꝓꝓ teuctoꝝ īsidias. media
eꝝgo ad orietez plana remanet. uineīsꝗ domestias arboriḷꜩ fecūda. et
portus ī ea cōcludiꞇᷓ tutus ꝗ ut auīt una cū coraca oli tenebꞇᷓ īsula.
Sz ꝓꝓ crebras tepestates. neuptuni atꝗ eoli terra tenax que īter duaꝝ
īsulaꝝ est inuenta maꝛe efficiatur ꞇᷓ coraca ab illa parꞇᷓ die ac nocte
muniutur.

# Corfu

## Cristoforo Buondelmonte

*1420*

## 1 : 350,000 approx

CRISTOFORVS BONDELMONT DE FLORENCIA PRESBITER NVNC MISIT CARDINALI IORDANO DE VRSINIS MCCCCXX [*Cristoforo Buondelmonte priest of Florence sent this work to Cardinal Giordano Orsini 1420*]. *Hand-coloured chart*, MS *on vellum, 250 × 180 mm. Plane projection north to the left. From Buondelmonte's* MS Liber Insularum Archipelagi [*Book of the Islands of the Archipelago*]. *Florence 1420. Latin text. Seventy-seven descriptions of islands. The title is derived from an acrostic based on the initial letters of each chapter.*

---

The earliest documents of navigational significance in the collections of the National Maritime Museum are two copies of the same work, one on vellum, the other on paper—a manuscript description of the islands of the Greek Archipelago written in 1420. Though the text is not specifically nautical, the plans of the various islands are closely related to the sea charts of the time and to the Italian *portolani* or pilot-books.

The plan reproduced here, taken from the vellum copy, shows the island of Corfu, then under Venetian rule, together with the adjacent coasts of Greece and Albania. Nominally, north is to the left but, even taking into account an easterly magnetic variation, this orientation is incorrect because the actual coast runs almost NW–SE.

All the plans are boldly coloured in water paints—green for sea and trees, uncoloured for plains, brown for mountains, and red and yellow for buildings and antiquities.

Many of the Latin descriptions have a nautical slant, as can be inferred from the following short extract:

> This island that is first to be described is Kerkyra, or Korkyra, so called from the ancient king of that name, and now known as Corfu. It is about 100 miles in circumference around the coast, and towards the south it is very mountainous, and there the trees produce much valonia or tannin. On the promontory of Amphipolis is the castle of Sancti Angeli, or the Holy Angels, that is strongly fortified and visible to sailors at sea from afar off . . .

Almost all we know of CRISTOFORO BUONDELMONTE (fl 1406–22) stems from the book itself. A member of a distinguished Florentine family, Cristoforo left his birthplace about 1406 and spent eight years in Rhodes, then the headquarters of the Knights of St John, during which time he took Holy Orders. About 1414 he began his journeys in the Greek Archipelago on behalf of his patron, Cardinal Giordano Orsini, collecting Greek MSS as well as data for his books. Orsini, who died in 1438, served as

legate in an attempt to negotiate peace in the Hundred Years' War between England and France.

Buondelmonte's first work was a description of the island of Crete (then under Venetian control), dedicated to Niccolò Niccoli in 1417; his second was the *Liber Insularum Archipelagi*, the subject of this note. In the Biblioteca Medicea Laurenziana in Florence exists his codex *Descriptio Cicladum . . .* [Description of the Cyclades] containing maps of northern Europe.

The *Liber Insularum* was an important work because, although it was never printed, it became the prototype for several subsequent *isolarii*, notably those of Bartolommeo dalli Sonetti (1485 and 1532, see Chart III), Henricus Martellus (c 1490), Benedetto Bordone (1528), Tommaso Porcacchi (1572), Antonio Millo (1591), and Marco Boschini (1658). In his book Buondelmonte describes in Latin seventy-seven islands of the Greek Archipelago from the Ionian Islands to Constantinople, at that time still under Byzantine rule.

At the end of the preface, Buondelmonte explains to his patron: 'You will find that when you string together the red letters at the beginning of each chapter, they form your name and mine, and the date on which this work was finished'. The resulting acrostic has been transcribed at the head of this page.

The copy from which this chart is taken is, however, unfinished, lacking the red initial letters for each chapter, though possessing an elegant 'C' at the head of the preface. This frustrates the acrostic but the writer has inserted small initials in black ink as a guide to the rubrication that was never carried out. An example can be seen in the illustration: the first word should be *Supra*, and some way to the left of the ornate *U*, is a small capital *S*.

## Bibliography

Anonymous MS notes in Italian, c 1800, bound into the front of NMM's vellum copy of Buondelmonte's *Liber Insularum* (1420), MS P13.

Legrand, E. *Description des Iles de l'Archipel par Christophe Buondelmonti, version Grècque par un anonyme, publiée d'après le manuscrit du Sérail, avec une traduction Française et un commentaire* (Paris, 1897)

Sinner, L. de. *Christoph. Buondelmonti . . . Librum insularum arcipelagi e codicibus parisinis regiis nunc primum totum edidit, praefatione et annotatione instruxit Gabr. Rud. Ludovicus de Sinner* (Leipsig and Berlin, 1824)

Waters, D. W. *Rutters of the Sea—Sailing Directions of Pierre Garcie* (1967)

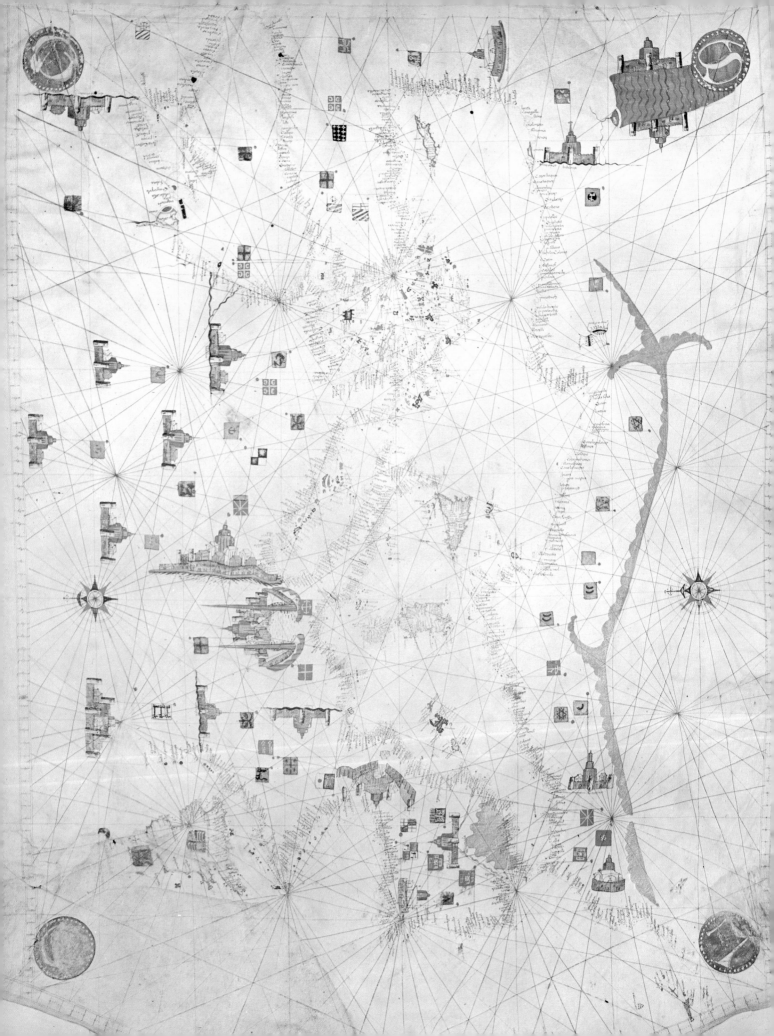

# Mediterranean and North East Atlantic

## Jacobo Bertran & Berenguer Ripol

### 1456

### 1 : 6,5000,000 approx

*No title. Signed on neck:* JACHOBUS BERTRAN ET BERENGARIUS RIPOL COMPOSUIT HANCH CARTAM IN CIVITATIS BARCHIAE ANNO ANATIUITATE DŇ M̃.CCCC.L.SEXTO [*James Bertran and Berenguer Ripol composed this chart in the city of Barcelona in the year of the birth of Our Lord 1456].Hand-coloured* MS *chart on whole skin of vellum, neck to the left, approx 980 × 630 mm. Plane projection.*

Though most scholars are agreed that there may have been some form of nautical chart in classical times, the sea chart as we know it evolved in Italy, probably in the first half of the thirteenth century; the first specific reference to a chart being used in a ship came in a description of the second crusade of St Louis of France in 1270. The earliest surviving chart is known as the *Carte Pisane*, so called because it was said to have come from a Pisan family when it was bought by the Bibliothèque Nationale in Paris in 1829. It is unsigned and undated but, from internal evidence, seems to have been drawn about 1300.

In area covered and in general appearance (except for embellishments), the chart reproduced here is very similar to the *Carte Pisane*, even though it was produced 150 years later, being drawn in 1456 by two Catalan cartographers in Barcelona, then in the kingdom of Aragon. It is of the type which in the nineteenth century became known as a 'portulan chart', because its construction was based on the sailing directions—chiefly the compass bearings and estimated distances between ports and headlands—contained in the contemporary *portolano*, or Italian pilot-book.

Though this chart has special Catalan characteristics, to be mentioned later, it is in fact typical of the manuscript charts drawn anywhere in the Mediterranean area right up to about 1650. It is drawn on a whole skin of vellum. (Sometimes they were cut up to form a book, as in Chart X.) It is overlaid with a system of rhumbs, that network of direction-lines showing the 'winds' or points of the compass that characterised almost all sea charts right up to the nineteenth century. Using these rhumbs, with a pair of dividers, the navigator could find the course to steer.

Placenames are written inland continuously round the coasts from north to south, so the chart has to be rotated to read them in sequence. The names of ports are in red, other names in black. The chart is embellished with national flags at the appropriate points—useful if, for example, a Christian is not to land inadvertently on a Moslem coast. Constantinople, which had fallen

to the Ottoman Turks in 1453, already has a Turkish flag. The Moorish kingdom of Granada, coloured green, was still in existence, for the Moors were not finally driven from the Iberian Peninsula until 1492.

There are vignettes of the principal cities concerned with commerce and pilgrimage, among which the following can be recognised: Santiago de Compostela in NW Spain, Barcelona, Avignon (*Auinyo*), Genoa, Venice, Jerusalem (*Santcepulcia*), Cairo (*Babilonja*), and Fez. The Red Sea is coloured red and the island of Rhodes red with a white cross (this last continued on Italian charts even after the Turkish conquest of the island in 1523).

Three features seen here are peculiar to Catalan charts: the waved appearance of the Red Sea (seen also in the Baltic in other Catalan charts); the green snakelike appearance of the Atlas and the mountain ranges; and the 'disks of the winds' at the four corners and the neck—G (*greco*) is north-east, S (*silocho*) is south-east, L (*libeco*) is south-west, P (*ponente*) is west (at the neck), M (*maestro*) is north-west—taken from the traditional Mediterranean compass of eight winds.

Only three charts signed by Jacobo Bertran are known for certain, dated 1456, 1482, and 1489. Berenguer Ripol seems to have been a pupil of Bertran but no example of his work other than that reproduced here is known.

Catalan cartographers worked extensively in Catalonia, Majorca, Sicily, Italy, and France from the fourteenth to the seventeenth centuries, the families of Oliva and Prunes being particularly active. One of the measures taken by Prince Henry the Navigator (see Chart VI) about 1419 was to procure the services of Mestre Jacomo of Majorca, a distinguished Catalan cartographer and astronomer.

## Bibliography

Pastor, J. R. & Garcia Camarero, E. *La Cartografia Mallorquina* (Madrid, 1960), particularly 82 and 198

*Periplus*, 16 *ff*

Winter, H. 'Catalan Portolan maps and their place in the total view of cartographic development', *Imago Mundi*, XI (1954), 1–12

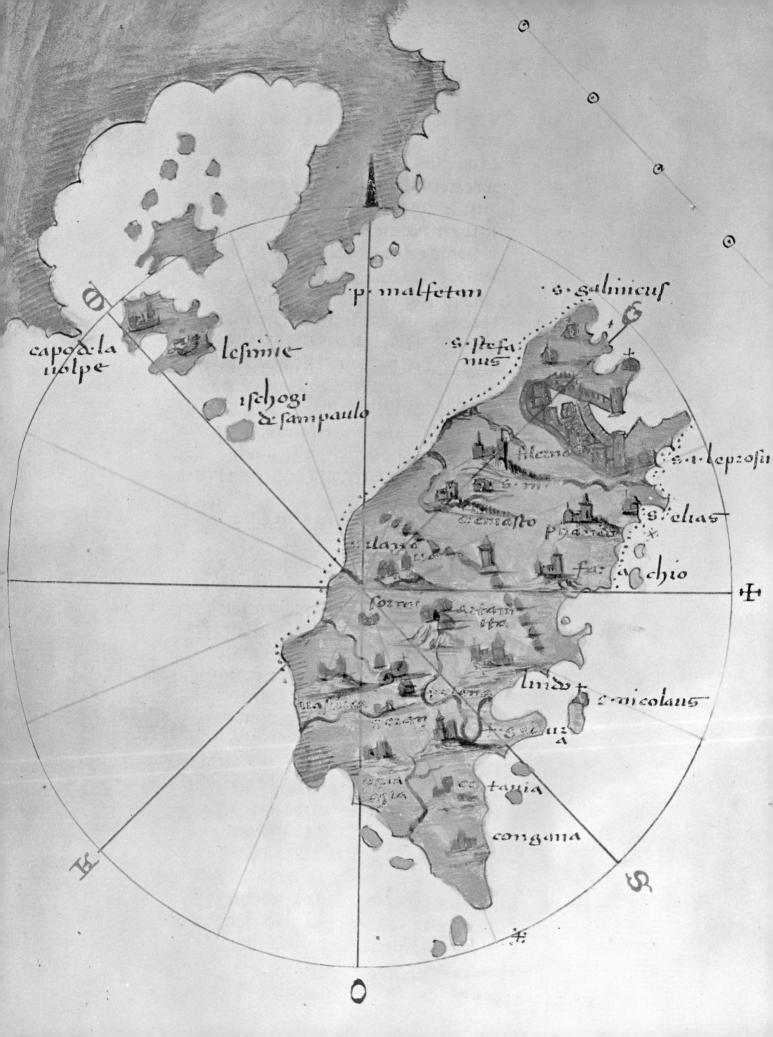

# Rhodes

## Bartolommeo Dalli Sonetti (Zamberti)

### c 1485

### 1 : 550,000

*Relevant text entitled* PER RODI [*For Rhodes*]. *Hand-coloured manuscript plan on vellum, 270 × 180 mm. Plane projection. From untitled and undated manuscript island-book signed on f 4r :* PER ME BON VENETIAN BARTHOLOMIO DALI SONETI : VER COMPOSITOR [*By me, good Venetian Bartolomeo Dalli Sonetti, true composer*]. *Venetian text in verse. Fifty-eight leaves, 280 × 200 mm.*

---

Illustrated opposite is a copy of an MS chart of the island of Rhodes, drawn by a Venetian shipmaster about 1485, and Fig 1 is a woodcut version of the same chart, printed and published in Venice in the same year. Both are illustrations from Sonetti's *Isolario*, or island-book, based broadly on Buondelmonte's *Liber Insularum* of 1420 (see Chart I), but written in verse. Sonetti's was the first island-book to be printed.

While there may be some doubt whether Buondelmonte's illustrations can be considered as sea charts, there can be none about Sonetti's. He says that they were constructed with the aid of a compass, and each chart has the eight-pointed Mediterranean compass rose. Most have scales of distance. Offlying rocks are indicated by the symbols ∺ and +, the same as those used on charts today. Rocky and other inhospitable shorelines are indicated. Sonetti's island plans, then, have the distinction of being the first *printed* sea charts.

When the chart reproduced here was drawn, Rhodes was under the control of the Knights of St John of Jerusalem, who remained there until 1523, when they were driven out by the Turks, to settle eventually in Malta.

The sonnets are written in the Venetian dialect. The first of the two dealing with Rhodes starts as follows:

*For Rhodes*
Those who want to join this island
    And her elect inhabitants, known as the Company of
                Knights Believers
    Must set no sight on earthly things
    But love the holy and divine.
In summer the island is full of fine roses
    That comfort the senses with their sweetness.
    From these the island takes its name
    For from roses 'Rhodes' in Greek derives.
Her ancient cities once played host
    To many Lords of nearby Asia Minor
    now called Turkey . . .
Then the land was nobler and greater
    But earthquakes reduced her once proud towers to ruin

Sonetti's real name was Bartolommeo Zamberti, called by himself and known by others as '*da li sonetti*' because of his liking for that kind of poetry. He was probably the same Zamberti, known as Bartolommeo Turco mentioned in Leonardo da Vinci's notebooks as having supplied information about the Black Sea and the Caspian. In the text he says that he has been to the Greek Archipelago fifteen times, first as an officer, then as captain, of a ship. His *Isolario* has forty-nine charts covering the islands of the Greek Archipelago, including Crete and Cyprus. Unlike Buondelmonte, Sonetti covers the Dodecanese but not the Ionian Islands.

The first edition with woodcut charts was printed in Venice about 1485 by Guilelmus de Panceretto Tridinensis (called *Anima mia*). There is no title page but, like Buondelmonte, Sonetti indulges in a word game: the first three lines of the prologue form a cryptogram dedicating the book to Giovanni Mocenigo, Doge of Venice from 1478 to 1485. Some scholars say this cryptogram also indicates a date of 1485.

The second edition was printed in Venice in 1532 and was updated by the addition of a woodcut of the oval map of the world drawn by Francesco Rosselli about 1508 (see Chart IV).

## Bibliography

Almagià, R. *Enciclop Italiana*, XXXV, 174

Destombes, M. *Catalogue des cartes gravées au XV e siècle* (Paris, 1952), No 52

Legrand, E. . . . *Christophe Buondelmonti* . . . (Paris, 1897), xxxii *Periplus*, 71–2

Skelton, R. A. *Introduction to facsimile edition of Bordone's* Isolario *(1528)* (Amsterdam, 1966)

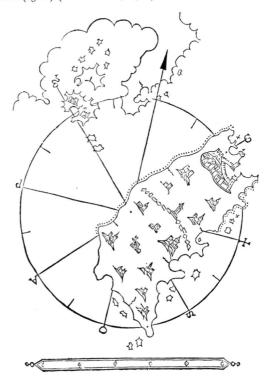

*Fig III–1*. The woodcut (printed) version of Sonetti's chart of Rhodes

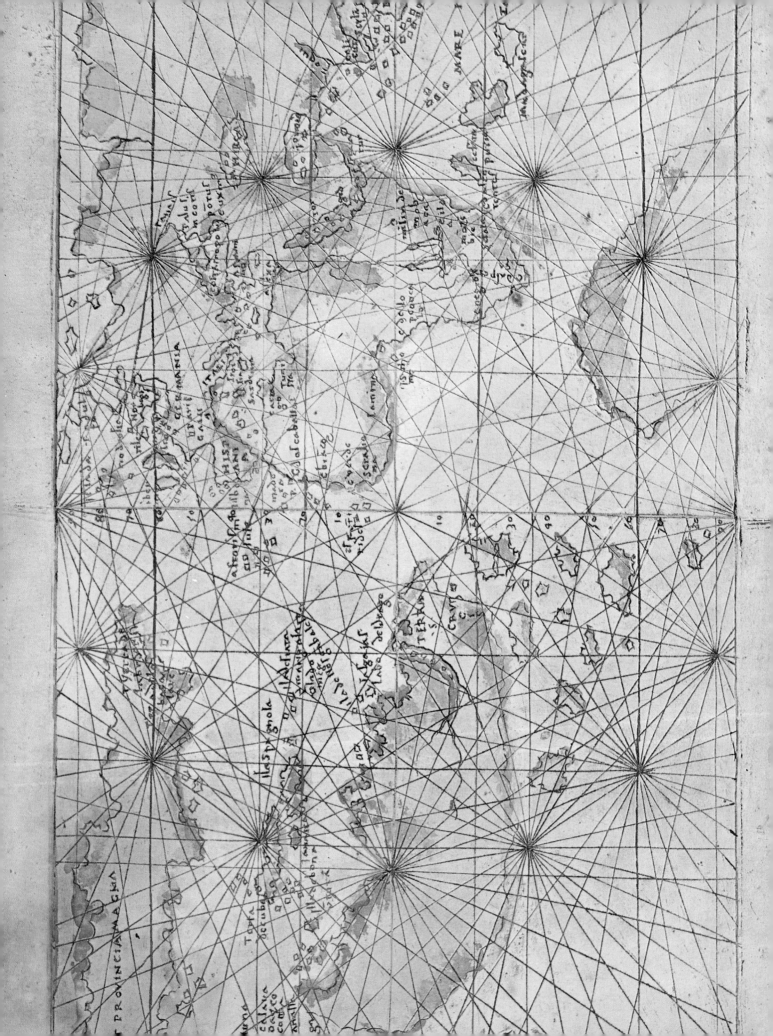

# The World

**Francesco Rosselli**

*c 1508*

## 1 : 140,000,000 approx

*Unsigned hand-coloured copper engraving on vellum, 140 × 284 mm. Plane projection. Folio 1 of a two-folio book. Folio 2 is an oval planisphere signed* F. ROSELLO FLORENTINO FECIT [*F. Rosselli of Florence made it, reproduced here as Fig IV–1*].

When Columbus sailed westwards in 1492, he was seeking a new route to the Indies—to Cathay—to China. To the end of his life he held to the belief that the lands he had discovered were indeed part of Asia; but not all cartographers agreed, and the chart illustrated here shows the somewhat confused attempt of a Florentine cartographer (working in Venice) to reconcile these new discoveries with the old geography of Ptolemy and Marco Polo.

This important chart is one of the earliest printed sea charts to show any part of the New World. Drawn about 1508, not long after Columbus had returned from his fourth voyage, it records the discoveries of Columbus, Hojeda, and Vespucci for Spain in the Caribbean (1492–1504); of John Cabot for England (1497); of the Cortereal brothers for Portugal in Newfoundland and Labrador (1497 and 1500–1); and of Cabral and Vespucci for Portugal in South America (1500 and 1501–2). It also takes into account other discoveries resulting from Vasco da Gama's voyage to Calicut round the Cape of Good Hope in 1498 and return in 1499.

On behalf of the new geography, the South American mainland, with the Antilles to the north, is shown as an island of continental size, rather closer to Asia than to Africa. On the other hand, Newfoundland and Labrador appear as part of Asia, thereby conforming to Ptolemaic geography, while the names bestowed by Columbus on features in Central America are shown against South-east Asia, because Columbus maintained that it was Catigara (Indo-China) that he had discovered on his fourth voyage.

The author of the chart, FRANCESCO ROSSELLI, was a member of one of Florence's most distinguished families and was born there in 1447, son of Lorenzo and younger brother of Cosimo, the artist. Following family tradition, Francesco first became a painter, and it was in Hungary between 1480 and 1494 that he first started drawing maps.

Returning to Florence in 1494, he set up at the Costa San Giorgio as cartographer, blockmaker, and printer. In 1504, leaving his business in charge of his son Allessandro, he went to Venice, where he spent the next four years, and it was here that he produced his world chart. He returned to Florence in 1508 and is believed to have died about 1513.

He is best known for the Contarini-Rosselli mantle-shaped world map of 1506, held to be the earliest printed map to show any part of the New World, the only known copy of which is in the British Museum.

As can be seen, the chart here is beautifully coloured with brush and pen. Hitherto it had always been thought to be entirely in manuscript. However, during researches connected with the writing of this book, the black detail on this so-called MS chart was closely compared with a photograph of the only printed copy then known, an engraving from the Landau-Finaly collection, now in the Biblioteca Nazionale Centrale in Florence. They proved to be identical! Haphazard scratches and other blemishes of the original plate have been faithfully reproduced on both copies. So our chart has proved to be an engraving after all.

It is a great tribute to Rosselli's skill as an engraver that this fact should have escaped detection for so long.

## Bibliography

Almagià, R. 'On the cartographic work of Francesco Rosselli', *Imago Mundi*, VIII (1951), 27–34 (his nos 9 and 10 on p 29)

Crinò, S. 'L'atlante inedito di Francesco Rosselli e la sua importanza nell'evoluzione cartografica del periodo delle grande scoperta', *Comptes rendus du Congrès International de Géographie* (Amsterdam, 1938), 153–63

Crinò, S. 'I planisferi di Francesco Rosselli dell'epoca delle grande scoperte geografiche', *La Bibliofilia*, XLI (1939), 381–405

Fiorini, M. *Sfere terrestri e celesti . . .* (Rome, 1899), 93–7

Harrisse, H. *Découverte et évolution cartographique de Terre-neuve . . .* (London–Paris, 1900), 65–70

Heawood, E. 'A hitherto unknown world map of AD 1506', *Geographical Journal*, LXII (1923), 279–94

Nunn, G. E. *World map of Francesco Roselli drawn on an oval projection . . .* (Philadelphia, 1928)

Skelton, R. A. *Introduction to facsimile reprint of Bordone's Isolario (1528)* (Amsterdam, 1966), VIII–X

*Fig IV–1.* Rosselli's oval planisphere

# North America — East Coast

## (Probably by Girolamo Verrazano)

*1529, corrected to 1540*

## I : 29,000,000

*Detail from unsigned and undated World Chart, hand-coloured* MS *on vellum whole skin, neck to the left, 710 × 1,080 mm.*

Only about twenty-five years elapsed between the drawing of Rosselli's nautical world chart (Chart IV) and the drawing of the original parts of this one (see Fig 1 below), but tremendous changes are evident, particularly in what today would be called the western hemisphere. North America is no longer joined to Asia; South America is not far off its true shape, being joined to North America by the Isthmus of Panama; and the Pacific has begun to make its appearance.

These changes are the results of many voyages of exploration, including those of Giovanni Verrazano, but, above all, of Ferdinand Magellan's discovery of a way from the Atlantic to the Pacific round the south of America in 1520. To all intents and purposes, the outline seen on this chart was to remain the shape of the known world for almost half a century—until Drake's circumnavigation changed the shape of South America, until the rounding of Cape Horn in 1615, until the Dutch discoveries on the west coast of Australia in 1616–29, and until Tasman's discoveries of the east coast of New Zealand and of Tasmania in 1642–3. It was not until Cook's voyages nearly 250 years later that it became possible to fill in the details in eastern Australasia and the Pacific and to produce the world map we know today.

The chart reproduced here has been attributed to the Florentine GIROLAMO VERRAZANO, brother and shipmate to Giovanni Verrazano, who explored the coast between Florida and Cape Breton Island—he gave his name to the narrows in the Hudson River between Brooklyn and Staten I—on behalf of Francis I of France between 1523 and 1528. Girolamo accompanied his brother on all these three voyages, from Dieppe, and witnessed poor Giovanni and six others being eaten by cannibals on one of the Antilles in 1528—which horrible scene he described to Giulio Giovo, who recorded it in verse.

The detail opposite shows the mythical Sea of Verrazano cutting North América in two halves, a fiction that persisted long enough to affect the projects of Hakluyt and Raleigh fifty years later and which was closely connected with the equally mythical Straits of Anian (see Chart XXIX). This fantasy was born in 1524, when Giovanni Verrazano in the *Dauphine* looked across the Cape Hatteras sandspit and saw what he assumed to be an ocean 'bathing the limits of India, China and Cathay'—in fact, the Pamlico Sound. The land to the north he named *Verrazana*, that to the south *Yucatanet*, and the narrow sandy isthmus joining the two, *Arenas*—all of which are marked here.

The North American coast seems to trend ENE–WSW instead of the real NNE–SSW, because magnetic instead of true bearings were used for laying down meridians. Among the names to the north identified by Destombes are *bonivetto* (Delaware Bay), *angholeme* (Manhattan), *p. sicuro* (New York), *refugio* (Newport), and *armelline sirtes* (Cape Cod). Further north, there is *R. Grande* (Bay of Fundy, shown with a Spanish flag), *baccaliaio* (Nova Scotia), *terra delle Mollie* (Cape Breton I), and, north of the Cabot Strait, *terra laboratoris inuenta pro Regem anglie* (Newfoundland, with sandbanks along the southern coast, shown as part of the mainland because the Strait of Belle Isle was not at that time known).

The chart is graduated with two sets of meridians, the original set in ink with the prime meridian passing through the west point of Palma in the Canaries (*FORTUNATE*); a second set in pencil, with longitudes unmarked, based either upon the west point of Madeira (*lamadera*) or upon the centre of Flores in the Azores (*aflore, LIAZORI*), which happen here to be exactly 10° apart. The coastline is drawn in green, the placenames in black and red, the border in red.

## Bibliography

Cumming, Skelton & Quinn, 80–4

Destombes, M. 'Nautical charts attributed to Verrazano (1525–1528)', *IM*, XI (1954), 57–66

Destombes, M. 'La Cartographie Florentine de la Renaissance et Verrazano', *Giornate Commemorative di Giovanni da Verrazzano* (Florence 1970), 33–7

Wroth, Lawrence C. *The Voyages of Giovanni da Verrazzano 1524–1528* (1970), 172

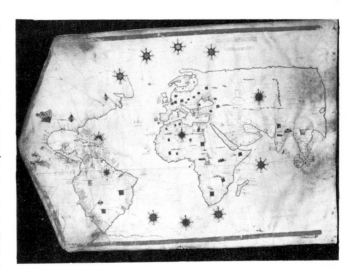

*Fig V–1.* Verrazano's world chart complete

# VI

## *Atlantic Ocean*
## (Probably by Pedro Reinel)

### c 1535

### 1 : 13,500,000

*Western part of chart of Atlantic. Unsigned and undated. Hand-coloured MS chart on two sheets of vellum pasted together. 805 × 1,217 mm. Plane projection.*

---

At the beginning of the fifteenth century trade between Europe and Asia was by way of the Black and Mediterranean Seas and almost entirely in the hands of the Italian maritime states of Venice and Genoa. Prince Henry the Navigator (1394–1460), son of a Portuguese king and an English Princess, determined to reach the source of European gold in Africa and to wage a crusade against Islam by sea.

So started the Age of Discovery!

Eventually, helped by the revenues of the Order of Christ, of which Prince Henry was Grand Master, the Portuguese found a seaway to the East by sailing southwards and eastwards round Africa. Cape Bojador, just south of the Canary Islands, was passed in 1434, Cape Verde in 1444, the Cape of Good Hope (by Bartholemeu Dias) in 1487, and, in culmination of the Portuguese efforts, Calicut on the Malabar Coast of India was reached by Vasco da Gama in 1498. Ormuz and Malacca, the west and east gates to the Indian Ocean, together with Goa, were all in Portuguese hands by the time this chart was drawn; Macao near Canton was settled in 1557.

The chart of the Atlantic, part of which is reproduced opposite, was drawn about 1535 and has been attributed, on handwriting evidence, to Pedro Reinel. The Portuguese father-and-son team of Reinel—Pedro and Jorge—flourished between 1480 and 1565. Of the ten known charts attributed to the Reinels, drawn between 1483 and c 1540, only three are signed and none are dated.

In the early period, almost nothing is known of them. As we have said in the Introduction, they had some connection with the Spanish preparations for Magellan's voyage round the world but, in 1524, they refused an offer to work in Spain and returned to Portugal.

In 1528 João III issued a charter to each as 'master of charts and navigation compasses', granting an annuity of 15,000 reis to Pedro and 10,000 reis to Jorge. The latest chart ascribed to Pedro is the chart reproduced here, and to Jorge one dated c 1540. Jorge is quoted as being 'master of nautical charts in [the King's] repository' in 1563–4 and as being 'sick, old, and poor' in 1572.

The eastern side of this chart, only the centre third of which is reproduced here, covers Europe and Africa from the Black Sea to Walvis Bay. On the west, the North American continent is given the name *Mundus nobgr* (presumably Norumbega, later New England). The west coast of South America is complete only to the latitude of Chimbote in Peru.

Coastlines are shown in green, placenames in black and red, islands in red, blue, or brown, and flags in their proper colours. There are views of the cities of Jerusalem, Cairo, Constantinople (?), Venice, and Lisbon, and of the castle of Mina on the Gold Coast. One factor to be taken into account in the dating is that it does not show the discoveries of Jacques Cartier in Canada in 1534, when he sailed through the Strait of Belle Isle and explored the Gulf of St Lawrence.

The latitude scale seems to coincide with Pope Alexander VI's line of demarcation, laid down in the Treaty of Tordesillas of 1493, giving Spain all discoveries west of a meridian 370 leagues west of the Cape Verde Islands. Brazil, Newfoundland, and Labrador are here on the Portuguese side of the line; however, there is a Portuguese flag against Nova Scotia, west of the scale, presumably in recognition of the discoveries of the Cortereal brothers of 1500–2.

## Bibliography

Caraci, G. 'Anonymous nautical map of the Atlantic', *Tabulae Geographicae Vetustiores in Italia Adservatae*, III (Otto Lange, Florence, 1932), 46–61, Plates XLII–L

Destombes, M. 'The Chart of Magellan', *IM*, XII (1955), 70

*HPC*, II, 207

*PMC*, I, 43–4, Plate 14. Also I, 19; V, 3–4

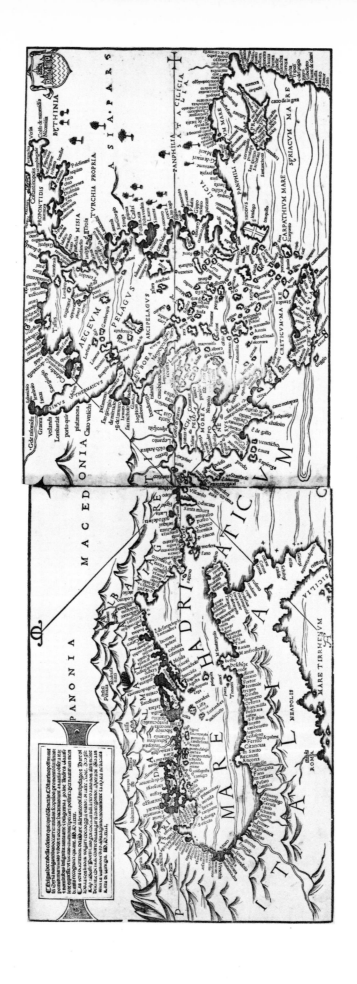

# VII

# *Adriatic Sea and Eastern Mediterranean*

## Giovanni Andrea Di Vavassore

### *1539-41*

### 1 : 2,500,000 approx

EXIGUA HEC TABELLA CŌTINET QUICQUID VENETIJS CŌSTANTI-
NOPOLIM . . . JOANE ANDREA VAVASSORE EXPRESSA . . . M.D. XXXIX
[*This small drawing contains all that may be met by sailors between
Venice and Constantinople, or Venice and Syria, including islands,
reefs, bays, headlands, harbours, and sea towns, and all those
places worthy of a name so far known to the sailor. Describing all
that may be remarked from existing sea charts. Drawn with all skill
and diligence by Giovanni Andrea Vavassore, 1539.*] LA VERA
DESCRITTIONE DEL MARE ADRIATICO: DI LARCIPELAGO: & MARE DI
ISOLA . . . OPERA DI GIOVANNI DA VAVASSORE DITO GUADGNINO . . .
CITTA DI VINEGIA. M.D.XXXXI [*The true description of the Adriatic
Sea, the Archipelago, and Sea of Soda (?), including all the names
of islands, reefs, bays, headlands, and harbours not otherwise
described than in the sea charts. The works of Giovanni Andrea
Vavassore, known as Guadgnino, newly printed in the city of
Venice, 1541*]. Woodcut chart on paper, 270 × 760 mm. Plane
projection.*

---

The earliest printed sea charts were the island plans of Sonetti
of about 1485 (Chart III). Printed *passage* charts did not appear
until more than fifty years later and Vavassore's woodcut shown
here has been claimed to be the earliest known.

Though undoubtedly derived from sea charts (see Vavassore's
own statements in the Latin title, translated above), its lack of
graduation or scale, and its tremendous distortion of shape, even
by sixteenth-century standards, make it somewhat doubtful
whether it should itself be considered as a sea chart. Forlani's
copper engraving of Homem's chart of 1569 (Chart XI) probably
has a better claim to be the earliest printed passage chart.

Little is known about Giovanni Andrea di Vavassore (fl 1520-
72), except that he was a prominent Italian engraver and printer
of books, working in Venice. Curiously, he was executing his
woodcuts at a time when most Venetian map-makers were
engraving on metal.

About 1545 he did a woodcut of Spain—'Nova descriptio
Hispaniae'—which is now extremely rare, and a number of later
maps of Italy by him have survived. This particular woodcut
charts in considerable detail the Adriatic, Aegean, and the islands
of the Eastern Mediterranean. Note the wealth of crowded names
along the shorelines, strikingly reminiscent of the style of the
earlier portulan charts.

No copies of the first (1539) edition are known. The one
reproduced here is the only known copy of the second (1541).

There was a third, identical in the chart itself but with Vavassore's
name removed from the title, published by Mattheo Pagano in
1558.

## Bibliography

Almagià, Roberto. 'La Carta d'Italia di G. A. Vavassori', *La
Bibliofilia*, xvi (1914), 81–8
Almagià, Roberto. 'Il Mappamondo di G. A. Vavassore',
*Rivista Geografica Italiana*, xxvii (1920)
Bagrow, Leo. *Giovanni Andrea di Vavassore . . . a descriptive
list of his maps* (1939)

# VIII

# The South Pacific

## Gerard Mercator

### 1541

### 1 : 35,000,000

*From a globe signed and dated* EDEBAT GERARDUS MERCATOR RUPELMUNDANUS CUM PRIUILEGIO CES: [CAESAREAE] MAIESTATIS AD AN:[NOS] SEX LOUANIJ AN:[NO] 1541 [*Published by Gerard Mercator of Rupelmonde under the patent of His Imperial Majesty for six years at Louvain in the year 1541*]. *Coloured gores, engraved on paper, globe diameter 420 mm.*

With the possible exception of Captain Cook, the only cartographer's name mentioned in this book that is bound to be familiar to the non-specialist reader is Gerard Mercator's. That this should be so, nearly 400 years after his death, is a measure of the service he rendered to cartography in general—and to navigation in particular—in first publishing a chart by the method that bears his name, still used today almost exclusively for ocean and coastal sea charts. Though strictly this method is not a map *projection*, it has traditionally been known as Mercator's projection and will be so referred to in this book, as on current British Admiralty charts.

On a Mercator chart a rhumb line appears as a straight line: a ship's track can, therefore, be plotted with a ruler. Mercator thus showed the solution to one of the most urgent problems that beset the fifteenth- and sixteenth-century ocean mariner using astronomy to find his latitude—how to portray a spherical surface (the Earth) on a flat piece of paper or vellum (the chart)—a problem not encountered by the ocean mariner's coasting counterpart.

The first map or chart to be published on Mercator's projection was his world chart of 1569, though he did not explain how it was constructed. However, Edward Wright, an English mathematician with sea experience, understanding its advantages, devised tables of Meridional Parts and gave a mathematical explanation, enabling cartographers to construct 'Mercator' charts and maps. First publishing in summary form in 1594, he gave fuller tables and explanations in 1599. The earliest chart on Mercator's projection reproduced in this book is one of Dudley's of 1647 (Chart XX).

But was there another solution to the problem of how best to present the curved surface of the Earth to the navigator? Instead of using a *plane* chart, could one use a *spherical* one—to wit, a globe? Globes had been used by navigators in the late fifteenth century (John Cabot, for example), but it was Mercator who, though nearly thirty years before he had shown the ultimate solution, determined to produce an up-to-date globe specially for the mariner—one on which rhumb lines would be shown in the same way as on the familiar plane chart (in point of fact, rather more correctly) and, furthermore, one on which the navigational stars would be shown in addition to details of land and sea. Two globes for the price of one!

Born GERARD KREMER in Rupelmonde, near Antwerp, Mercator (1512–94) entered the University of Louvain in 1530, studying under the famous mathematician and globe-maker Gemma Frisius, one-time pupil of Peter Apian.

On leaving university, Mercator, stimulated by Frisius, turned his attention to the manufacture of mathematical instruments and to cartography. His first engraved map was published in 1537 and his first globe—the terrestrial one shown opposite—in 1541. Its celestial counterpart was published in 1551.

In 1552, presumably so that he could be nearer his chief patrons, he moved to Duisburg on the Rhine, whence his most famous maps were published, including the vast nautical world chart of 1569, laid down on the new projection. Thereafter, he devoted himself to producing his *magnum opus*—his great *Atlas* (he himself is said to have been the first to have used the name), the last part of which was not published until a year after his death.

The globe is dedicated to Nicolás Perrenot (Chief Minister to the Emperor Charles V), who is believed to have suggested the project to Mercator.

It has a longitude graduation based on Fuerteventura in the Canary Islands. As already mentioned, the sea areas are covered with a network of rhumb lines while the first-magnitude stars are laid down in their correct positions in right ascension and declination. In addition, the ecliptic is shown, enabling the sun, moon, and planets to be plotted in pencil with the aid of an almanac.

In the Great Southern Continent south of the Pacific Ocean is the legend: 'Reader, where and in what subjects we have copied from the publications of other men will be pointed out in our booklet'. Alas, no such work by Mercator is known! In another legend, he states that his equatorial degree is equal to 500 stadia, or 60 Italian miles, 19 Spanish miles, 20 French miles, and 15 German miles.

## Bibliography

De Smet, A. *Les Sphères de Gerard Mercator 1541 et 1551* . . . (Brussels, 1968), preface

Osley, A. S. *MERCATOR. A monograph on the lettering of the maps, etc., in the 16th century Netherlands, with a facsimile and translation of his treatise on the italic hand and a translation of Ghim's VITA MERCATORIS* (1969)

Stevenson, E. L. *Terrestrial and celestial globes, their history and construction* . . . (New Haven, USA, 1921), 127–35

Waters (1958), 74, 220 ff

Wright, Edward, *Certaine Errors in Navigation* . . . (1599)

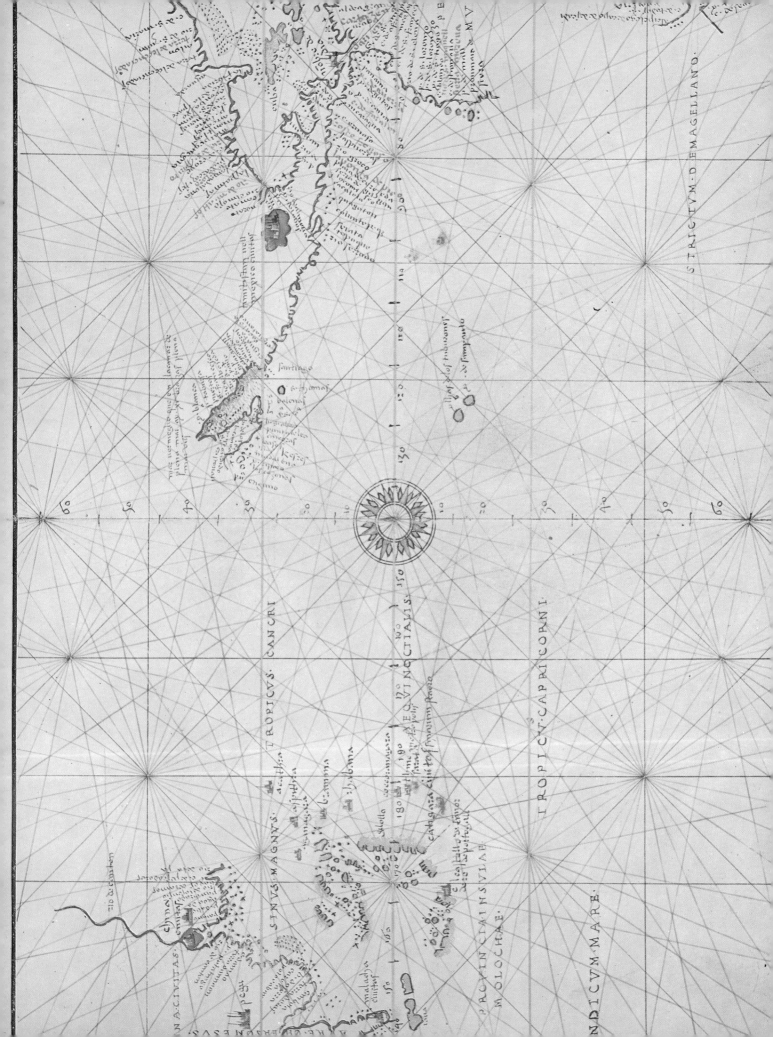

# IX

# Pacific Ocean
## Battista Agnese

### 1555

### 1 : 75,000,000

*[Pacific Ocean]. Unsigned and undated. Hand-coloured. MS on vellum, 207 × 307 mm (to edge of borders). Plane projection. From illuminated atlas of 25 folios of vellum, in which folio 7 (NW Europe) is signed and dated* BATTISTA AGNESE FECIT UENETIJS ANNO DN̄J 1555 DIES 24 MARCIJ. *[Battista Agnese made it in Venice in the year of Our Lord 1555 on the 24th day of March.]*

When in 1513, 'silent upon a peak in Darien', Vasco Nuñez de Balboa and his men (not Keats' 'stout Cortez') became the first Europeans to see the Pacific Ocean, they named it *Mar del Zur* —the South Sea—because they could see it trending southward. In 1520, when Ferdinand Magellan sailed out of the Strait that bears his name, he named that same ocean *Mar Pacifico*—the Quiet Sea.

The chart opposite shows the state of knowledge of the Pacific (then usually called the South Sea) about 1550. On the American coasts are the Strait of Magellan; the coast of Peru, explored by Francisco Pizarro's conquistadores in 1531-3; the Pacific coasts of Central America and Mexico, explored by Spain after 1520; and the peninsula and Gulf of California, explored by Francisco de Ulloa in 1539-40 and by Juan Rodríguez Cabrillo in 1542-3.

In the Central Pacific only two islands of the Marquesas Group, seen by Magellan in 1521, are marked. On the Asiatic side of the Pacific, the coast is well shown, from *Taprobana*— the old name for Ceylon here transferred to Sumatra—to some way east of Canton on the China coast, together with Java, Timor, and vestiges of Borneo, Palawan, the Moluccas (the Spice Islands in which *Gilollo* is today's Halmahara), and the Philippines—all except the last in the Portuguese sphere of influence. There are no signs of Korea or Japan in the north, or of New Guinea, Australia, or New Zealand in the south—these last had yet to be discovered.

This chart shows one of the earliest indications of depth of water to be seen on a sea chart, though not in the form of soundings as we know them.

Near the head of the Gulf of California, here coloured red, is the legend *Mar Vermeglio que en lacanar [lacanal] de plena mar ay xi brazas plena [baxa] mar viij* (Vermilion Sea where the channel at high water is 11 brazas, at low water 8). Agnese made two errors in this particular copy, so words used in other copies have been supplied in brackets.

This statement is presumed to have stemmed from the lost charts of Ulloa, who discovered the Colorado River at the head of the Gulf in 1539. He reported the river water had a reddish tint, so gave the Gulf the name of Vermilion Sea (thereby distinguishing it from the Red Sea).

The unit of depth was the *braza*, the Spanish fathom and equivalent to the French *brasse*—the length of two arms outstretched—a unit used since the earliest times to define the amount of line hauled in by the leadsman, and hence the depth of water, after he had taken a sounding.

As might be inferred from the high proportion of Italian charts reproduced in this book so far (six out of nine), the centre of commercial cartographic activity between 1450 and 1550 lay in Italy—first in Florence, later in Venice. True, the most up-to-date sea charts came from Portugal or Spain but the sale of these were restricted as far as possible by the authorities to their own nationals, and relatively few survive.

The chart opposite, executed by BATTISTA AGNESE (fl 1536-64), a Genoese working in Venice, is of exquisite draughtsmanship and illumination and a superb example of the best that Italy could produce at that time. Despite the competition from printed maps and charts, there was obviously a ready market for the hand-produced atlases on vellum such as Agnese had to offer, as witness the fact that more than seventy of his atlases produced between 1536 and 1564 survive today, more than 400 years later. His total production could well have exceeded 100.

Scholars have argued that the high quality and small scale of the charts make it unlikely that these atlases were ever used at sea. Be that as it may, they are in typical portulan style and as such deserve representation in this book.

Agnese achieved something of a scoop by being the first cartographer to show California on a chart—one similar to this one, but dated May 1542—based on Ulloa's discoveries.

## Bibliography

Destombes, M. 'Les plus anciens sondages portés sur les cartes nautiques . . .', *1ᵉʳ Congrès International d'Histoire de l'Océanographie* (Monaco 1966), 204

Wagner, Henry R. 'The Manuscript Atlases of Battista Agnese', *Papers of the Bibliographical Society of America*, XXV (1931). The NMM's *P12* is his No LVII (pp 94-5); *P24* is unrecorded

Wagner, Henry R. *Cartography of the Northwest coast of America* . . . (Berkeley, 1937; reprinted Amsterdam, 1968), No 4

Wagner, Henry R. *Spanish voyages to the Northwest Coast of America in the sixteenth century* (San Francisco, 1929), 300, Pl VI

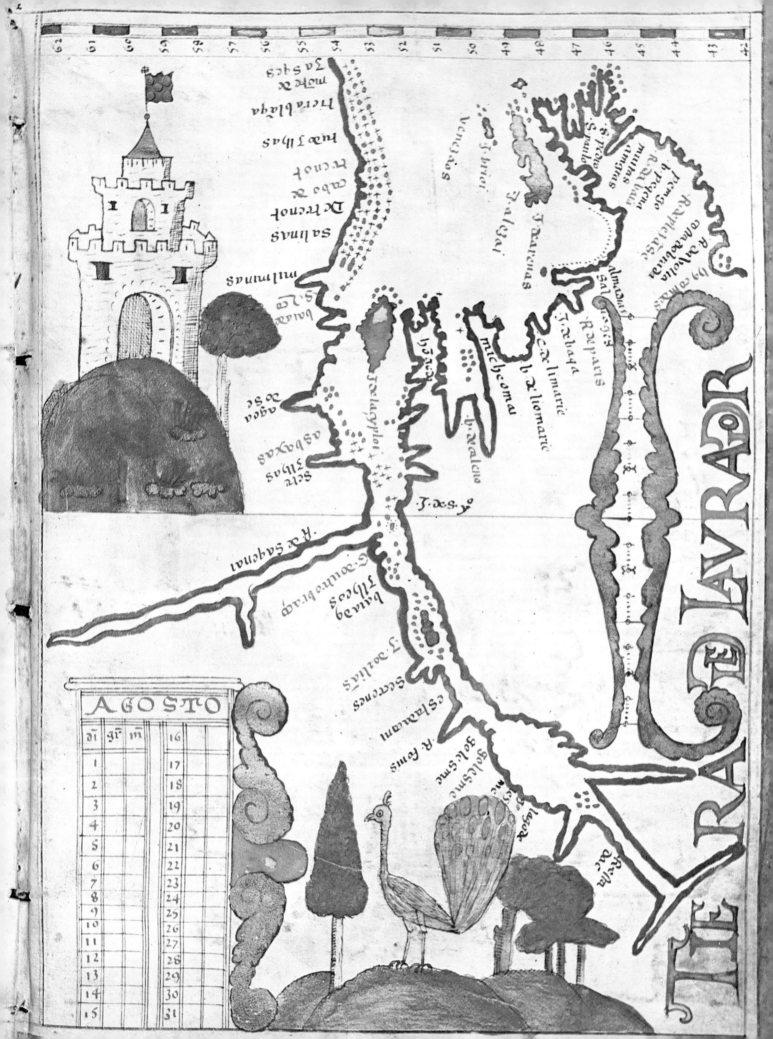

# X

**Bibliography**

Cumming, Skelton & Quinn, 90
*PMC*, 73–6, Plate 196c

# *Gulf of St Lawrence*
## Portuguese

*c 1555*

1 : 16,000,000

TIERA DE LAVRADOR [*Land of Labrador*]. *Unsigned and undated. Hand-coloured* MS *on vellum, 205 × 145 mm. Plane projection, north to the left. From chart-book of 15 sheets of vellum, 170 × 240 mm, folded in half and drawn on both sides.*

---

As Verrazano had failed to find for France a westerly sea passage through North America to Cathay in 1524–8 (see Chart V), Francis I despatched Jacques Cartier of St Malo on the same quest in 1534, with instructions to explore the St Lawrence River. In three voyages between 1534 and 1543, Cartier sailed through the Strait of Belle Isle (thereby proving that Newfoundland was an island) and explored the Gulf and River St Lawrence as far as the present site of Montreal (named by Cartier himself). But no sea strait was found and, in 1543, France abandoned organised exploration in the region for almost sixty years.

The chart reproduced opposite—north is to the left—shows the Gulf and River St Lawrence from Cape Breton Island at top right to Montreal at bottom right. It was drawn by a Portuguese hydrographer, probably for a Spanish customer, about 1555. It shows the results of Cartier's discoveries and was probably based on some recent French map such as that of Vallard of 1547. Names which may be identified are *I. de la cyploi* (Anticosti I), *b. de calcno* (Baie de Chaleur), *R. de Sagenoi* (Saguenay River), *I. dorliãs* (Isle d'Orléans), *estadacani* (near Quebec), and *lago de golesme* (Lac Pierre).

The Portuguese chart-book from which this was taken contains (a) charts covering the passage from Europe to India round Africa, and (b) charts of the east coast of America from the Strait of Magellan to Labrador, together with (c) a page giving the *Regiment of the North Star*—the rule for correcting the observed altitude of the Pole Star to find latitude (see Fig X–1).

To enable the mariner to find latitude by observing the altitude of the sun at noon, monthly solar declination tables are given, one or more to each page, supposedly covering the four-year cycle. In fact, the tables were not completed beyond December of the second year (on the chart of East Africa) so the chart opposite has a blank declination table for August of year four.

Unfortunately, one leaf is missing from the book, covering on one side the Eastern Mediterranean, and on the other the Gulf of Mexico and the eastern seaboard of the United States.

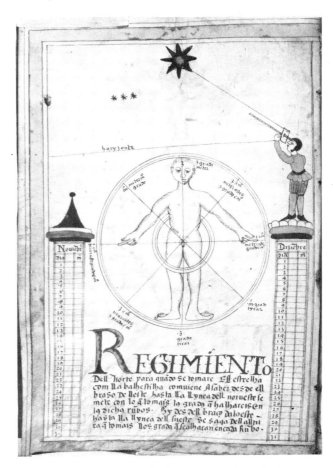

*Fig X–1.* The *Regiment of the North Star*—the rule for correcting the observed altitude of the Pole Star for finding latitude (Folio 15v)

# Central Mediterranean

## Diogo Homem (cartographer) and Paolo Forlani (engraver and publisher)

### 1569

### 1 : 7,750,000

*Detail from:* [*Mediterranean Sea*] AL MOLTO MAG:<sup>CO</sup> S ILS GIACOMO MVRARI MIO.S. SEMP̄: OSS:<sup>MO</sup> . . . DA VINEGIA IL P° D'OTTOBRE L'ANNO M.D.LXIX. IN MERZÉRIA ALLA LIBRERIA DALLA NAUE . . . PAOLO FURLANI VERONESE [*To the Most Magnificent Signor the Signor GIACOMO MURARI, my ever-respected Lord . . . From Venice, the First of October, 1569. At the bookshop of the Ship in the Mercaria . . . Paolo Furlani of Verona*]. *Hand-coloured engraved chart, 490 × 824 mm to outer edge of printed sheet. Plane projection.*

---

The chart opposite, published in Venice in 1569 by a Veronese engraver using information supplied by a Portuguese cartographer, was the first plane chart on a scale large enough to be useful at sea to be printed by the copper-engraving process, which for 350 years, until lithography began to take over in the 1920s, was to remain the primary method for producing sea charts.

Forlani starts a long and fulsome dedication by saying that there are plenty of printed *maps*; he goes on:

> . . . but as its [the Earth's] description according to the use of mariners has not yet been published, nor the sailing chart, a thing

necessary to every sort of person, I being desirous of serving the world, am doing so, and have requested and obtained from S Giocomo Homem, Portuguese, a man excelling in this, a description of Europe and part of Africa and Asia, according to the use of mariners . . . and other things needed for good navigation . . .

This chart is specifically mentioned by Ortelius in the 1579 and subsequent editions of *Theatrum Orbis Terrarum*. It was reissued several times and copied by Lafreri in 1572, when Homem's name was kept on the chart but Forlani's omitted.

The copy reproduced here has at some stage been hand-coloured, with stylised views of cities added in manuscript in the portulan tradition. Map- and chart-sellers were always willing to provide coloured copies at extra cost, thus helping the printed chart to compete with its attractive but more expensive hand-drawn counterpart.

The lines of crosses west of Corsica and Sardinia, and the star in the Gulf of Sidra (*bottom right*), represent dangers which appeared on most charts of the time, but have since proved non-existent.

PAOLO FORLANI of Verona (fl 1560–74) was an engraver and map-publisher who worked mostly in Venice. He also made MS copies of sea charts.

DIOGO HOMEM (fl 1547–76) was the son of the famous Portuguese hydrographer Lopo Homem. Diogo was first heard of in London in 1547, an exile from Portugal, but is assumed to have worked with his father in Lisbon before that date. From 1568 to 1576 he was in Venice. He was a prolific provider of sea charts and one of the outstanding hydrographers of the sixteenth century. Twelve of his charts and twelve of his atlases survive.

## Bibliography

Destombes, M. *Une Carte inedité de Diogo Homem, circa 1566* (Coimbra, 1970), 5

*PMC*, II, 35–7

*Fig XI–1.* The chart complete

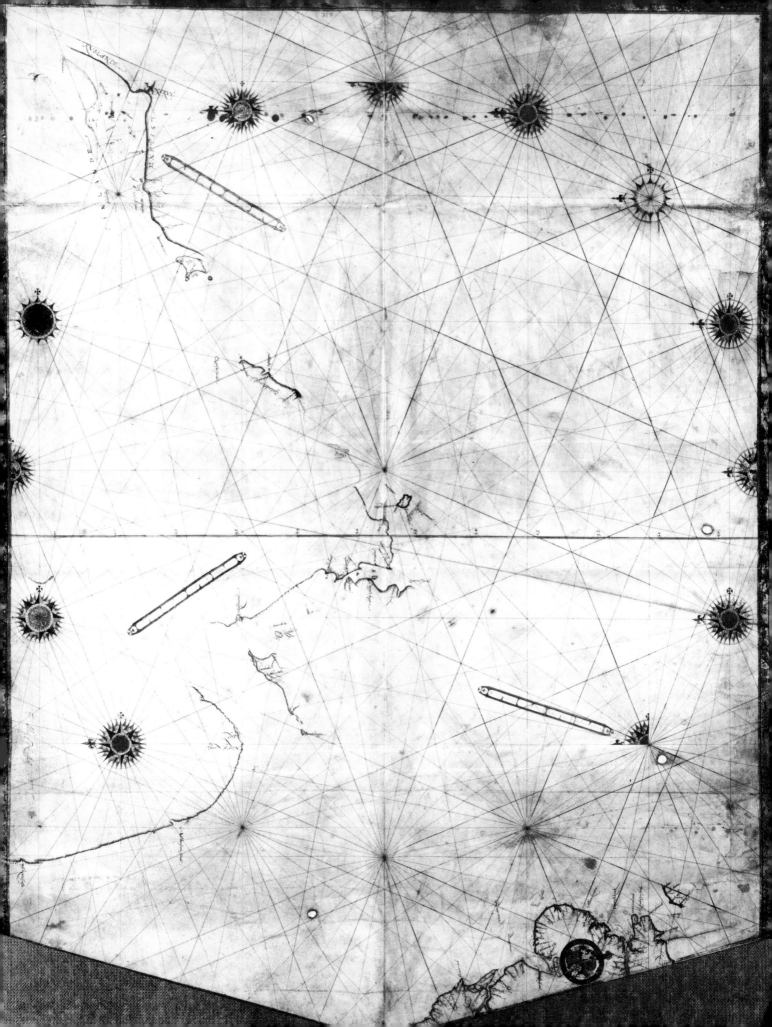

# XII

# The Passage from England to the Gulf of Finland

## William Borough

*c 1580*

**1 : 2,020,000**

[*North and Baltic Seas*]. MADE BY MR. W. B[OROUGH]. *No date. Coloured* MS *chart on vellum whole skin, 720 × 960 mm. Plane projection.*

---

This, the earliest English chart in the book, was drawn by William Borough, sometime Master of Trinity House and Chief Pilot of the Muscovy Company, Queen Elizabeth's first and most distinguished hydrographer, and an experienced navigator trained by Sebastian Cabot.

Though the chart looks unfinished, it was probably designed specifically to show only those coasts that would be seen by a ship on passage from England to Narva in the Gulf of Finland —the passage taken by ships of the Muscovy Company, outward in April–June, homeward in September–November, from 1558 to 1581, when Narva was in Russian hands. Tar, cordage, and timber were the main imports from the Muscovy trade—all essential for our shipping.

The three bar-scales are aligned approximately to the courses made good on such a passage—NNE from England to the Skagerrak, with the Naze of Norway to port and Jutland to starboard; SE by S round the Skaw and through the Sound to the Baltic; NNE from the island of Bornholm, leaving the islands of Öland and Gotland to port, to the entrance of the Gulf of Finland; then up the gulf with *FINLANDE* to port and *LYFLANDE* (now Estonia) to starboard.

On the north shore of the gulf (drawn in pecked line), the ports of *Elsenforse* (Helsinki) and *Wyborow* (Vyborg) are marked; on the south, *Narve* (Narva)—the main port of call—and *Revel* (Reval, now Tallinn). There was at that time no city in *RUSLANDE* at the hand of the gulf where Leningrad now stands.

In marked contrast to contemporary Mediterranean-drawn manuscript charts, decoration is restricted to the compass roses (each one has a different motif, the top and bottom showing half polar projections) and to the royal coat of arms over East Anglia. This is a plane chart, the latitude scale being linear.

WILLIAM BOROUGH (1537–98) was born at Northam in Devon, son of John à Borough, a sea captain of note, and younger brother of Stephen, also a distinguished navigator. In 1553, at the age of sixteen, William served as ordinary seaman under his brother in Richard Chancellor's expedition, organised by Sebastian Cabot to search for the North-east Passage to Cathay. Between 1556 and 1575, William Borough spent his time voyaging to St Nicholas (Archangel) or Narva, or travelling in Russia on behalf of the Muscovy Company. He succeeded his brother Stephen as Chief Pilot of the Company.

About 1579 William entered the service of the Crown, becoming Comptroller of the Navy in 1583 and later Treasurer of the Queen's Ships. In 1585, he became Master of Trinity House. He commanded the *Lion* in Drake's raid on Cadiz in 1587— earning Drake's displeasure for his caution—and the galley *Bonavolia* in the Thames during the Armada year of 1588.

As a hydrographer he is known particularly for his *Discours on the Variation of the Cumpas or Magneticall Needle* (1581), in which he discusses rhumb lines and Mercator's chart of 1569, as well as magnetic variation. Charts signed by him are preserved in Hatfield House, the British Museum, the National Maritime Museum, and Trinity College, Dublin.

## Bibliography

Waters (1958), 153, 156–62

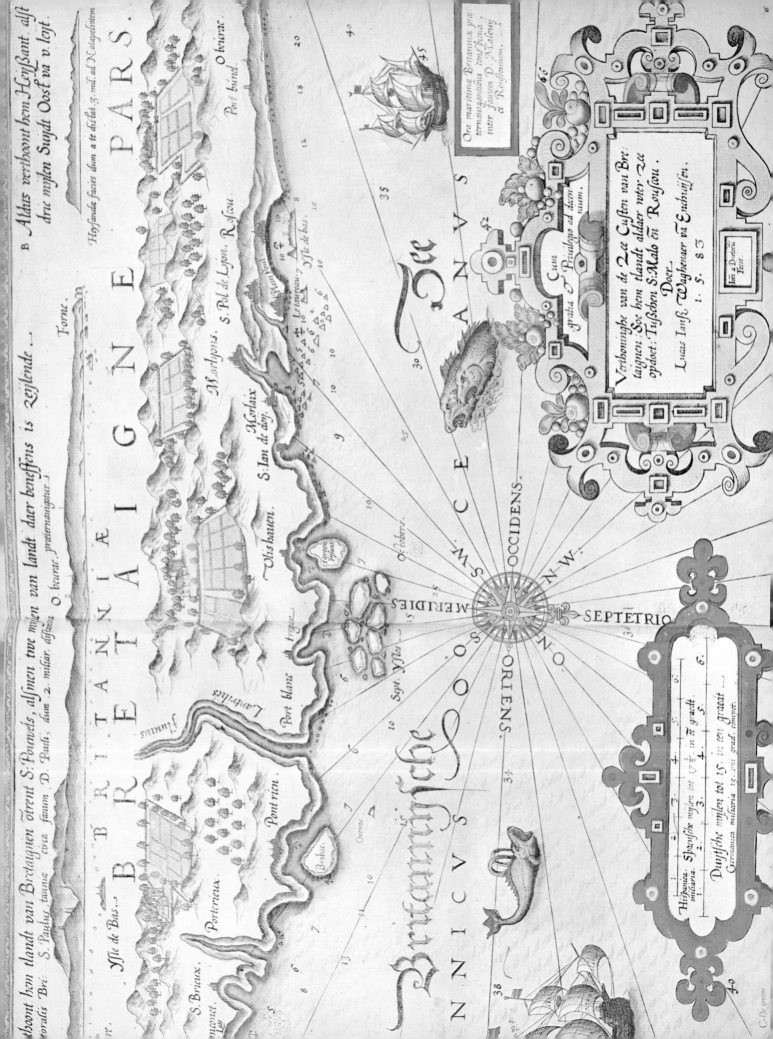

# The Coast of Brittany

Lucas Janszoon Waghenaer

*1583*

I : 395,000

ORA MARITIMIAE BRITANNIAE . . . INTER FANUM D MALOUIJ ET ROUSCOUIUM. VERTHONINGHE VAN DE ZEE CUSTEN VAN BRETAIGNEN . . . TUSSCHEN S. MALO EN̄ ROUSCOU. DOER LUCAS IANSZ WAGHENAER VĀ ENCHUIJSEN. 1583. *Signed Waghenaer and the engraver Joannes à Doetecum. Dated 1583. Coloured chart, engraved on paper, 325 × 640 mm. Double cartouches in Latin and Dutch: From Waghenaer's* SPECULUM NAUTICUM. *Leyden, Christopher Plantin. 1585. Latin text; two parts in one. Folio. 45 coloured charts.*

---

The publication of Waghenaer's *De Spieghel der Zeevaert* in 1584 was a landmark in the history of the sea chart. It was the first printed sea atlas with charts and sailing directions assembled systematically in one book so as to give the mariner all the hydrographic information he needed about a specific area. The charts themselves contained many new features, to make them self-sufficient for pilotage purposes—the showing of soundings (in fathoms at half-tide), the first time this had been done on a printed chart; the deliberate distortion of the coastline to allow areas of difficult pilotage such as harbours and river mouths to be shown on an enlarged scale; and the placing of the coastal views on the charts themselves rather than in the text. The charts covered the principal ports and the coasts of Western Europe from Norway to Spain.

LUCAS JANSZOON WAGHENAER (1533–1606) was the celebrated Dutch hydrographer and pilot of Enkhuizen. *De Spieghel der Zeevaert* was originally published at Leyden in 1584, and its great popularity with mariners and sea traders led to many subsequent editions up to 1615, with versions in Latin, Dutch, English, French, and German. It was so influential that, until the eighteenth century, sea atlases were often referred to in England as 'waggoners'.

Part one of the first Dutch edition comprised twenty-three charts engraved on copper by Joannes à Doetecum, and a second part appeared in 1584, with twenty-one additional charts. The first Latin edition, the *Speculum Nauticum* of 1586, was translated from the earlier Dutch versions by Martin Everaerts of Bruges and contained forty-four charts, each supported by a descriptive text on the reverse.

The chart illustrated is one of a series of four in the atlas in which Waghenaer delineates the entire coast of Brittany. Particularly apparent is the fine draughtsmanship and engraving —in the elaborate cartouches, the compass rose, sea monsters, and sailing ships. More practically, note the representation of anchorages, rocks, and shoal water (especially off Morlaix and St Pol).

## Bibliography

Arnold, J. I. *Bibliographie de l'œuvre de Lucas Jansz. Waghenaer* (Ghent, 1880)

Gernez, D. 'The works of Lucas Janszoon Waghenaer', *The Mariners' Mirrour*, xxiii (1937), 332–56

Koeman, IV, 465–501

Koeman, Dr C. 'The history of Lucas Janszoon Waghenaer and his Spieghel der Zeevaerdt' [introduction to the facsimile edition] (Amsterdam/Lausanne, 1964)

Skelton, R. A. *Bibliographical note to the facsimile edition of the* Spieghel der Zeevaerdt (Amsterdam, 1964)

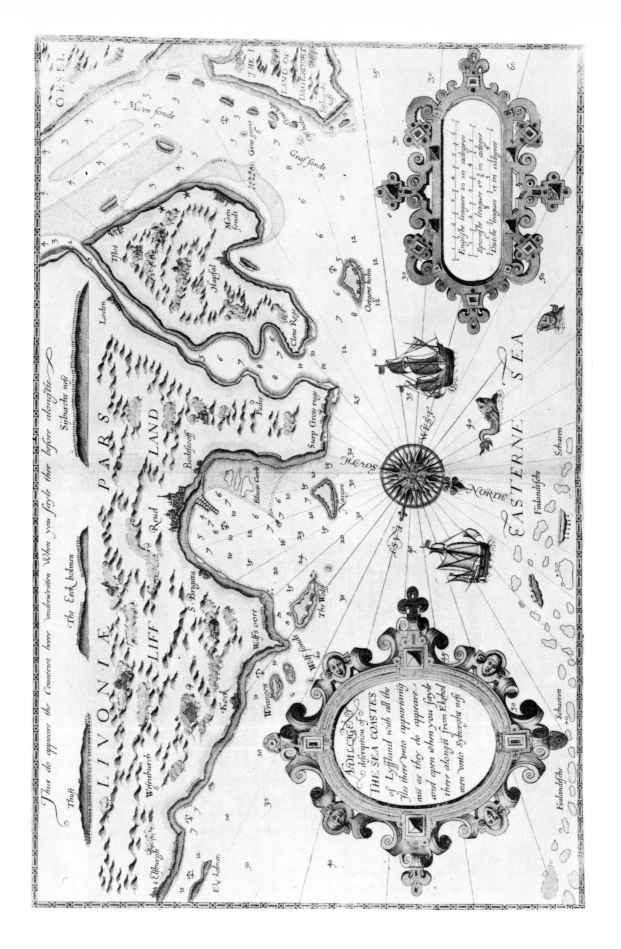

# XIV

# Baltic Sea. The Coast of Estonia and Bay of Tallinn

## Lucas Janszoon Waghenaer & Anthony Ashley

*c 1588*

1 : 420,000

*A DILLIGENT DESCRIPTION OF THE SEA COASTES OF LYFFLAND WITH ALL THE ILES THEREUNTO APPARTANING EENE AS THEY DO APPEARE AND OPEN WHEN YOU SAYLE THERE ALONGST FROM EKEHOLMEN UNTO SYBURGHS NESS. Unsigned and undated. Hand-coloured chart, engraved on paper, 330 × 505 mm. From the second part of Waghenaer's sea atlas* THE MARINERS' MIRROUR, LONDON; 1588. *English black-letter text. Two parts in one, with separate titles to each. 45 coloured charts. Folio.*

---

In 1585 Lord Howard of Effingham, Lord High Admiral of England, drew the Privy Council's attention to the value of Waghenaer's sea atlas *De Spieghel der Zeevaert* to English seamen. His work was '. . . esteemed by the chief personages of the grave counsell worthy to be translated and printed into a language familiar to all nations'. Thereupon, the Clerk of the Council, Sir Anthony Ashley, was instructed to supervise its undertaking. While most of the charts in the original Dutch work had been engraved by Joannes à Doetecum, it was decided to employ the services of four other distinguished cartographers and engravers for the production of the English edition—Theodor de Bry, Jodocus Hondius, Johannis Rutlinger, and Augustine Ryther. The charts are based on those that appeared in the earlier Latin and Dutch editions between 1584 and 1586, the main differences being the substitution of English cartouches and, in some charts, the insertion of dates and the engravers' names.

*The Mariners' Mirrour* was thus the first English sea atlas and, indeed, its charts were the earliest printed charts in English.

This chart of the coast of Livonia or Liefland (Estonia and NE Latvia today) belongs to the second part of Waghenaer's atlas, covering the east coast of England, Scandinavia, and the Baltic shore. It was just the type of chart needed by the English mariners and merchants who followed in the steps of Willoughby, Chancellor, and Jenkinson, for trade with the Baltic was developing and the first commercial links with Muscovy were being forged. It should be compared with Borough's smaller-scale manuscript chart already described (Chart XII). Note the delightful depiction of the wooded foreshores, anchorages and soundings, and the harbour quay at Revel (Tallinn); and Waghenaer's inclusion of coastline profiles at three important points, as an aid to pilots.

Another feature of Waghenaer's charts was the systematisation of the signs and symbols used, the first time this had been done. They were described and illustrated in his Introduction (Fig 1). Though the use of an anchor symbol to denote safe anchorages and of a cross to denote rocks had been used before, the system of buoyage seems to be an innovation. Note the black conical buoy shown off *Bloote Caerls*: according to the key, this was a buoy 'chiefly on the right hand of fairways on sailing out, painted black with pitch or tar'. It seems that the left side of the fairway was not normally marked though 'jutting out rocks' were marked by buoys painted white.

## Bibliography

Koeman, IV, 497–501

*Fig XIV-1.* Waghenaer's conventional signs and symbols

# XV

# Eastern Mediterranean and Black Sea

Joan Oliva

*1592*

## I : 10,000,000

*[Eastern Mediterranean and Black Sea]. Unsigned and undated. Hand-coloured* MS *chart on vellum, 203 × 270 mm. Plane projection. From* MS *vellum chart-book signed* IOAN OLIVO IN MISSINA. AÑO 1592.

---

This is an example of a manuscript chart of the Mediterranean which, instead of being drawn on a whole skin, has been drawn on smaller sheets of vellum, cut up and bound into book form. It was produced by a Catalan cartographer working in Messina in 1592 and is remarkably similar to the corresponding portion of the Catalan portulan chart already reproduced (Chart II), drawn 136 years before, in 1456. The geography of the Black Sea and the names round its shores have hardly changed at all, and in the Levant the changes have been far fewer than might have been expected.

Note the miniatures of sovereigns on this chart—the King of Russia brandishing his sword somewhere in Rumania and the Grand Turk in Anatolia. Other charts in the book cover the Mediterranean and North Atlantic as far as Brazil and Newfoundland, and depict the kings of France, Spain, Hungary, Poland, Fez, and Tunis.

JOAN OLIVA (fl 1580–c 1615) was a member of a large family of Catalan hydrographers, two of whom, Bartolomeu and Jaume, started working in Majorca before 1550 and then emigrated to Sicily and Italy. Charts signed by no less than sixteen different members of the Oliva family are recorded between 1538 and 1673, from Majorca, Messina, Naples, Leghorn, Florence, Venice, Malta, Palermo, and Marseilles.

Joan, believed to be the same as Joan Riczo, seems to have been the most prolific of this large family, thirty-three of his charts or atlases being recorded from Naples, Messina, and Marseilles (where he died). He is often confused with Joannes, who worked in Leghorn between 1622 and 1650.

## Bibliography

Destombes, Marcel. 'François Ollive et l'Hydrographie Marseillaise au XVIIᵉ Siècle', *Neptunia* 37 (Paris, 1955)

Pastor, J. R. & Garcia Camarero, E. *La Cartografia Mallorquina* (Madrid, 1960), 119–63. The atlas from which the chart illustrated is taken is not recorded by Pastor and Garcia Camarero

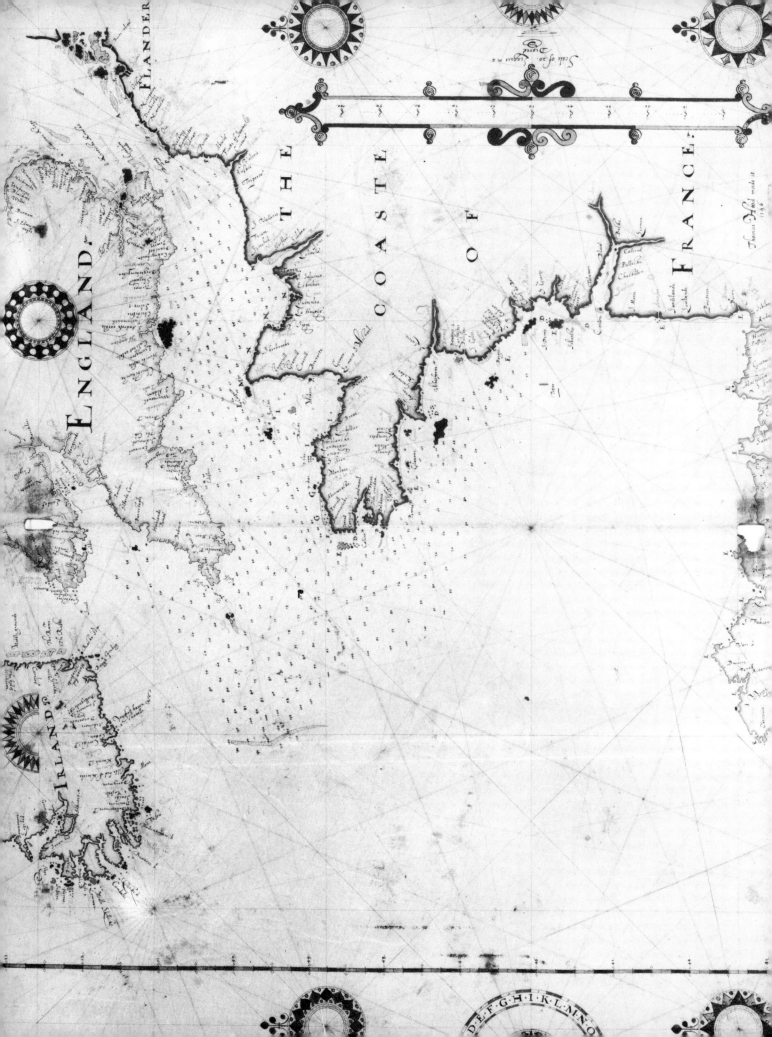

THE COASTE OF

ENGLAND.

FRANCE.

FLANDER.

IRLAND.

# XVI

# Bay of Biscay and English Channel

## Thomas Hood

## 1596

## 1 : 3,000,000

*No title. Signed* THOMAS HOOD MADE IT. 1596. *Hand-coloured* MS *chart on vellum, 405 × 532 mm. Plane projection.*

---

A sixteenth-century mariner obtaining a sounding of 100 fathoms when approaching the English Channel from the Atlantic knew that he was about 30 leagues, or 90 nautical miles, from danger—either Ushant or the Scillies. If the weather allowed, he could also take an altitude of the Sun at noon or the Pole Star at night to give him his latitude. The 'position lines' indicated by the sounding and the latitude would give a 'fix'—though a sixteenth-century navigator would not have used those terms—if a suitable chart were available.

The chart opposite was one of the earliest charts (perhaps the earliest) both to show soundings out as far as the 100 fathom line and to possess a latitude scale. It also shows a long narrow shoal, presumably the Great Sole Bank (well known to fishermen, as the name implies), running north and south some 25 leagues west of the Scillies, as well as giving tidal information for ports in the Low Countries, France, and Spain.

Drawn by a lecturer in mathematics and navigation, who apparently never went to sea, it shows by these innovations the growing scientific approach to navigation—an approach that had already made England a leader rather than a follower, as she had been before Elizabeth's reign, in navigational techniques and practice.

A further example of this trend may be seen in a printed chart of approximately the same area and date (not reproduced here) published by Edward Wright in 1599, only three years after Hood's manuscript chart was executed. In some aspects the charts by Hood and Wright have much in common: the coastline and soundings are so similar as to make it almost certain that these were copied from the same original; and roughly the same area is covered, though Wright's takes in the Azores but omits the Strait of Dover. On the other hand, there are some very important differences: Wright's is on Mercator's projection —the earliest known printed example—whereas Hood's was a plane chart; Wright's has information about magnetic variation, Hood's has tidal information; and, of course, Wright's was printed while Hood's was in manuscript.

The method of indicating tidal information was as suggested by William Bourne in his *Regiment of the Sea* of 1574. The letters against the various ports indicate the *Establishment of the Port* or *High Water Full and Change* (that is, the *apparent time* of High Water on the day of Full Moon ['Full'] or New Moon ['Change']). This is done in what today may seem a rather roundabout way, by indicating the bearing of the sun (or moon when at Full or Change) at the material time (whether or not it is above the horizon), using as a key the half compass rose on the west border of the chart, where each point of the compass (from north to south through east) is lettered from A to R: thus A = north = 12 midnight; E = north-east = 3 am; and so on to R = south = 12 noon.

For example, the letter E against Ushant indicates that, on the days of Full and New Moon, the time of High Water off Ushant is 3 am (and 3 pm). It was easy to find the time of High Water on other days by taking into account the moon's age, for each day of which the time of High Water was taken back one compass point (45$^m$ of time). Taking Ushant again (E = 3$^h$), when the moon is 4$^d$ old, the time of High Water would be E minus 4 points, that is A = north = midnight.

In fact, this ancient method is quite accurate and High Water Full and Change (expressed as a *time* in Roman figures, eg IV$^h$) was the standard method of giving tidal information for ports right into the twentieth century.

THOMAS HOOD (fl 1582–1611) was the son of a London merchant tailor and appropriately attended Merchant Taylors' School. He matriculated at Cambridge in 1573 and graduated finally as Master of Arts from Trinity College, Cambridge, in 1581. Soon afterwards, he started lecturing in mathematics in Leadenhall Street and Gracechurch Street in the City of London, turning to navigation in 1588. He was the author of many important works on navigation and kindred subjects, of which *The Mariners Guide . . . wherein the vse of the plaine Sea Card is briefelie and plainely deliuered, to the commoditie of all such as haue delight in Nauigation* of 1592 is particularly relevant to this commentary.

## Bibliography

Waters (1958), 144, 199

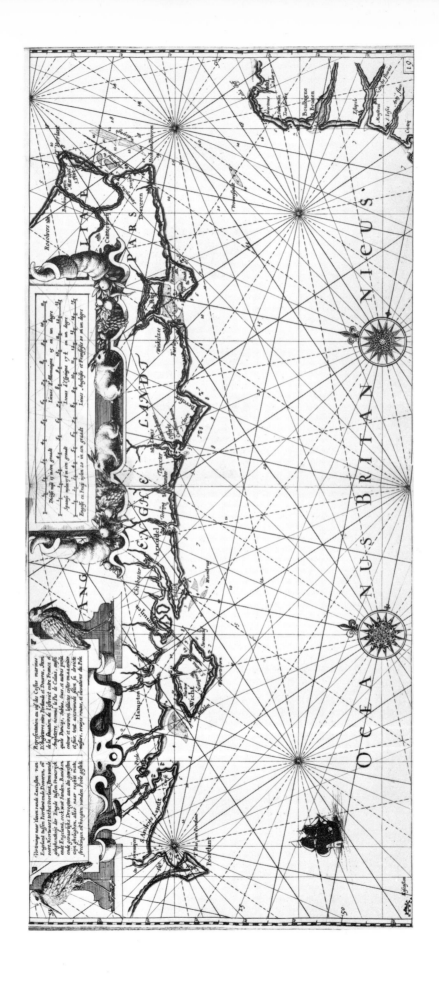

# XVII

# The South Coast of England between Portland and Dover

**Willem Janszoon Blaeu & Jan Jansson**

*c 1620*

1 : 615,000

**Bibliography**

Koeman, IV, 47–51
Skelton, R. A. *Introduction to the 1964 Amsterdam reprint of Blaeu's* The Light of Navigation (*1612*)

VERTONINGE NAAR 'TLEVEN VANDE SEECUSTEN VAN ENGELANT TUSSEN POORTLANT ENDE DOEVEREN . . ./REPRESENTATION AU VIF DES COSTES MARINES D'ANGLETERRE ENTRE PORTLANDE ET DOUVRES . . . [*Representation from life of the sea coasts of England between Portland and Dover*]. *Unsigned and undated. Uncoloured chart, engraved on paper, 245 × 545 mm. Double-cartouches, in Dutch and French. From Blaeu's pilot guide* THE LIGHT OF NAVIGATION BY WILLIAM IOHNSON. AT AMSTERDAM. PRINTED BY IOHN IOHNSON, DWELLING UPON THE WATERSIDE, BY THE OLD BRIGDE [SIC], AT THE SIGNE OF THE SEA-MAPPS. ANNO 1620 *Published as a new edition by Jan Jansson. Amsterdam, Jan Jansson, 1620. English text. Two parts in one, with separate titles to each. 42 charts. Oblong folio.*

---

Blaeu's pilot-guide *Het Licht der Zeevaert*, first published at Amsterdam in 1608, was a milestone in the development of marine cartography. Its forty-two charts accurately depicted the 'Western, Eastern and Northern navigation' in two books, and the charts were prefaced by a long and important instruction in the art of navigation. Blaeu's charts were an improvement on Waghenaer's, on which they were based. The coastline was less pictorial but more accurate. He discarded Waghenaer's practice of showing harbours, etc, on an enlarged scale and relegated coastal views to the text.

Blaeu's original work ran into many Dutch editions and was also translated into English and French. Though the text is in English, the charts themselves were not re-engraved for the English edition, and their cartouches and other inscriptions remain in Dutch and French. Unfortunately Blaeu's great rival, Jan Jansson, began publishing his own version of the pilot-guide in 1620, in direct competition. The same titles were used, including *The Light of Navigation* of the English edition, and the charts and text were closely copied. This situation spurred Blaeu into publishing, from 1623 onwards, an entirely new and much larger pilot-guide series, which we know as the *Zeespiegel* (111 charts).

The chart comes from the second part of the Jansson version of Blaeu's original English edition of *The Light of Navigation*. The title page of the atlas carries the anglicised form of both their names—William Iohnson (for Blaeu), Iohn Iohnson (for Jansson).

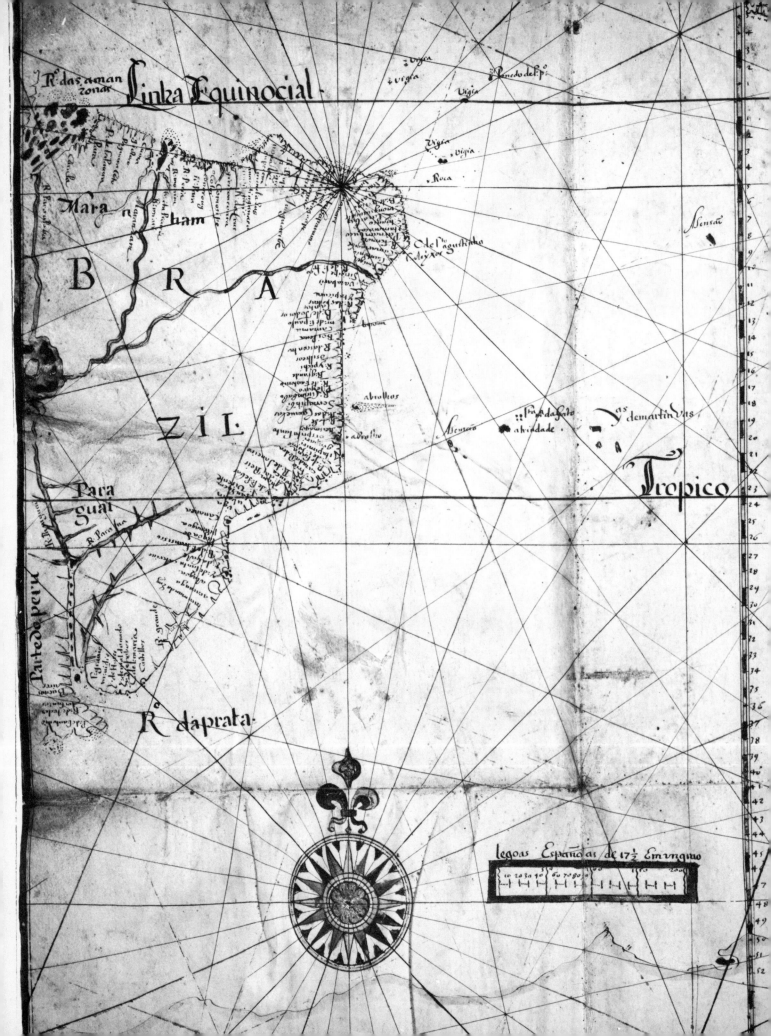

# XVIII

# South West Atlantic

## Antonio Sanches

### 1633

### I : 21,000,000

*Western half of untitled chart of South Atlantic, signed* ANTONIO SANCHES. AFES EMLISBOA ANNO 1633. *Hand-coloured chart on vellum, 355 × 950 mm. Plane projection. From untitled book of 6* MS *charts by Sanches and Joan Oliva.*

This Portuguese plane chart of the South Atlantic shows two geographical misconceptions—the Great Southern Continent, and the large lake in the centre of the South American continent.

The Great Southern Continent—*Terra Incognita Australis*—was that great land mass which some geographers said must cover the whole of the southern part of the Earth in order to balance the land masses of Asia and Europe in the north. It appeared on maps of the world from the time of Ptolemy onwards, and in some charts from the sixteenth century. By the seventeenth century, however, some geographers had begun to doubt its existence, or at least whether it extended as far north as latitude 50°S, as shown here.

Sanches has drawn the unknown coastline of the Southern Continent in yellow, whereas the known coastlines of Africa and America are in black. In view of the fact that it was 'undiscovered', he has perhaps overdone the detail—capes and islands and bays can be seen, while, on the *Terra Australis* coast south of Africa (on the half of the chart not reproduced here), he has drawn three large rivers. Though 'unknown' coasts were frequently shown on maps, they were seldom shown on charts and Sanches' chart is unusual in this respect.

The eighteenth-century geographers were sceptical about this unknown land mass, but its existence was not finally disproved until Cook returned home from his second voyage in 1775, having circumnavigated the Antarctic. Finally, in the late 1820s, sealers began to spread rumours of a real Southern Continent south of Cape Horn, rumours which were confirmed by James Clark Ross in HMS *Erebus* in 1841, when he discovered Antarctica, almost all of which is south of 67°S.

Sanches shows here in the Matto Grosso a large lake full of islands as the source of all the great rivers of Brazil, the *R. Parusaba* entering the sea at Pará at the mouth of the Amazon, the *Maranham* at Maranhão, *R. de S. Fr*°° (São Francisces) between Pernambuco and Bahia, and *R. Paraguai* in the River Plate (*R°daprata*). This particular fantasy is unusual on charts of this period. Such an idea was presumably suggested by a similar mythical lake shown at this time in many maps of Africa as the source of the Nile and other large rivers.

The surviving works of ANTONIO SANCHES (fl 1623–41) are a planisphere in the British Museum (1623), the charts of the North and South Atlantic in this atlas at Greenwich (1633), an atlas of sixteen charts in the Royal Library at The Hague (1641), and a chart in private hands in England (1637).

The book containing the chart opposite has six charts—four of the Mediterranean signed *Joannes Oliua fecit in Ciuitate liburni* [Leghorn] *año 1632*, and two of the Atlantic, both signed and dated by Antonio Sanches in Lisbon in 1633. This mixed authorship in a chart-book, particularly when the authors are of different nationalities, is unusual.

## Bibliography

*PMC* V, 18 and Plate 528B

# XIX

# Western Mediterranean

## John Burston

### *1638*

### 1 : 4,250,000

*Detail from chart of Mediterranean signed* MADE BY JOHN BURSTON DWELLING OUER AGAINSTE NEW GRAVELL LANE IN RADCLIFF HIWAY NEARE LONDON ANN° DOMIN 1638. *Coloured* MS *chart on vellum, laid down on linen (modern), 495 × 940 mm. Plane projection.*

---

Illustrated opposite is a manuscript chart drawn on vellum in England, where the demand for such charts persisted throughout the seventeenth century, despite increasing sales of printed sea atlases and waggoners. Their advantage lay in their durability, particularly in resisting damage from salt water. A few Dutch *printed* charts on vellum survive.

The demand for hand-drawn charts was satisfied by the so-called Thames school of platt-makers (a platt is a sea chart), which produced plane charts with systems of rhumbs and place-names written more or less in the Mediterranean portulan tradition, but with latitude scales, some soundings, and decoration usually limited to compass roses and bar-scales. These English charts were usually mounted on two or four hinged oak boards so that they could be folded up like a book or screen to protect the surface when not in use.

The English platt-makers nearly all worked in Radcliff or Wapping, in seventeenth-century London's dockland, between the Tower of London and Stepney, many of them dating their work from 'The sign of the platt'. The most important were John Daniell, Nicholas Comberford, John Burston, and John Thornton, and all the cartographers seem to have been members of the Drapers' Company, being successively apprentice and master—a relationship discovered by Professor Thomas R. Smith of the University of Kansas.

Though the school flourished largely in the seventeenth century, it had its origins in the sixteenth, its chart-making techniques being set by Sebastian Cabot and William Borough. The charts produced in the 1590s by Robert Norman (who worked in Radcliff and was well known also as a compass-maker) and Thomas Hood (who worked in the City and was a mathematics teacher, see Chart XVI) are obviously the models for those of Daniell, Comberford, and the others in the seventeenth century.

Illustrated opposite is part of the earliest Thames-school chart in the museum—one of the Mediterranean, drawn by John Burston in 1638, the year after he completed his apprenticeship. Like all Mediterranean charts of this scale for some years to come, it shows no soundings. A particular feature of the Mediterranean charts of the Thames school was the numbering of islands, which numbers were listed in tables round the borders. The table for the Balearics can be seen here.

JOHN BURSTON (fl 1628–d 1665?)—was apprenticed to Nicholas Comberford (see Chart XXII) in 1628. Charts signed by him still extant are dated between 1638 (this one) and 1665. John Thornton (see Chart XXX) was in turn apprenticed to Burston from 1656 to 1664.

On 18 February 1665 Samuel Pepys notes in his diary:

> . . . and took My Lord Sandwich's draught of the harbour of Portsmouth down to Ratcliffe, to one Burston, to make a platt for the King, and another for the Duke [of York], and another for himself; which will be very neat.

After visiting Burston several times to watch progress, he says on 5 March:

> Up, and Mr. Burston bringing me by order my Lord's platts, which he has been making this week. I did take coach and to my Lord Sandwich's and dined with my Lord; it being the first time he hath dined at home since his coming from sea . . . After dinner looked over the platts, liked them mightily, and indeed I think he is the most exact man in what he do in the world of that kind.

## Bibliography

Smith (1969)

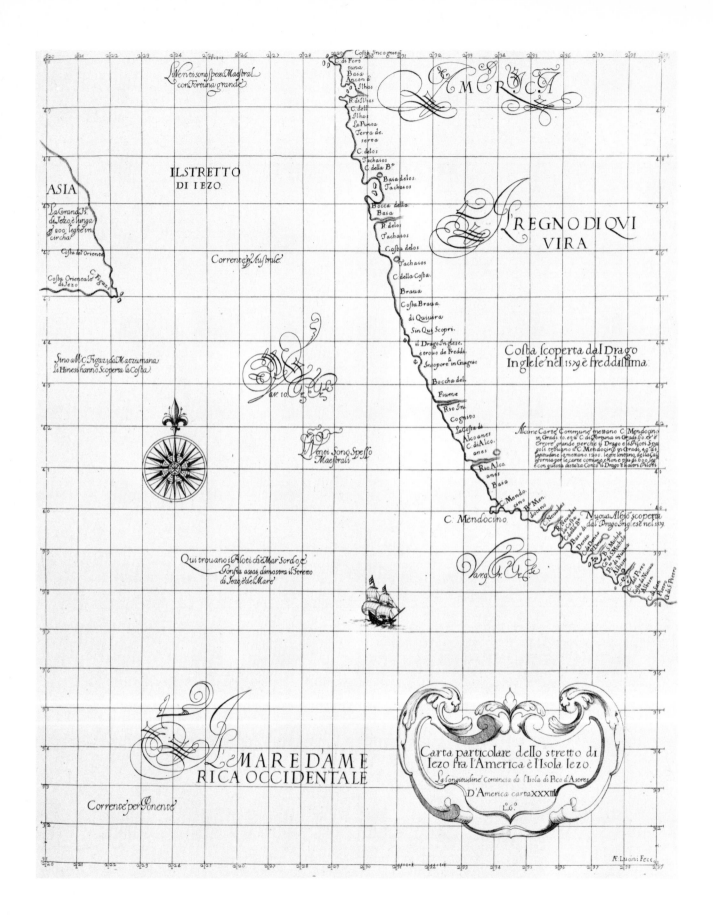

ASIA

ILSTRETTO
DI IEZO

AMERICA

L'REGNO DI QVI
VIRA

Costa scoperta dal Drago
Inglese nel 1579 è freddissima

C. Mendocino

Nuoua Albio scoperta
dal Drago Inglese nel 1579

L'MARE D'AME
RICA OCCIDENTALE

Carta particolare dello stretto di
Iezo fra l'America è l'Isola Iezo.
La longitudine comincia da l'Isola di Pico d'Asores
D'America carta XXXIII

A. Luini Fece

# XX

# The Pacific Coast of North West America

## Sir Robert Dudley

*c 1647*

1 : 4,800,000

CARTA PARTICOLARE DELLO STRETTO DI IESO FRA L'AMERICA È L'ISOLA IEZO . . . D'AMERICA CARTA XXXIII. [*Particular chart of the Strait of Jezo from America to the island of Jezo . . . of America, chart number 33*] *Signed* A[NTONIO] F[RANCESCO] LUCINI [*the Italian engraver*]; *undated. Uncoloured chart, copper-engraved on paper, size 365 × 462 mm. Single cartouche, in Italian. Mercator's projection. From Dudley's sea atlas* ARCANO DEL MARE. *Florence, Guiseppe Cocchini, 1661. Italian text, in six books, large folio, with separate engraved titles to each and numerous engraved plates and diagrams, including volvelles. 146 charts.*

---

This chart of the north-east Pacific is taken from Robert Dudley's monumental atlas *Dell' Arcano del Mare*, the first atlas to be published with all charts on Mercator's projection, the first sea atlas by an Englishman (though in the Italian language), and the first sea atlas to cover the whole known world.

SIR ROBERT DUDLEY (1574–1649) was an illegitimate son of the Earl of Leicester—minister and favourite of Queen Elizabeth—and brother-in-law of the circumnavigator Thomas Cavendish. Through the latter he became a close friend of the mariners John Davis and Abraham Kendall.

In 1594–5 Dudley voyaged to the West Indies with the *Earwig* and *Bear*, attacking Spanish shipping and exploring the Guiana coast. On returning to England he took part in Essex's raid on Cadiz in 1596, after which he was knighted. Later he got into matrimonial difficulties and lost favour at Court, which finally drove him into permanent exile. In 1605 he became a Roman Catholic and settled in Florence, where his skill as a naval architect and shipbuilder brought him fame and the patronage of royalty.

After many years' work his great atlas *Dell'Arcano del Mare* (Secrets of the Sea) was published in Florence in 1646-7. The work is arranged in six books, the charts occupying books ii and vi. A second enlarged edition—whence this chart comes—was published in Florence in 1661, twelve years after Dudley's death. In the preface the Italian engraver Antonio Francesco Lucini states that the preparation of the plates for the atlas had taken twelve years to complete and consumed 5,000 lb of copper in the process.

The charts are notable for the beauty of the engraving and the elaborate calligraphy. This chart of part of the Pacific coast of NW America is of special interest because it shows the much-

disputed site of Drake's anchorage at Nova Albion in June–July 1579, during his voyage of circumnavigation.

## Bibliography

Leader, John T. *Life of Sir Robert Dudley* (1895)
*NMM Cat iii*, part 1, 386–8

# XXI

# The North Sea

## Jacob Aertsz Colom & Arnold Colom

*1656*

## I : 2,900,000

PASCAARTE VAN DE NOORD ZEE/DOOR ARNOLD COLOM T AMSTERDAM BY HET WATER BY DE NIEUWE-BRUGH INDE LICHTENDE COLOM *1656*. [*Chart of the North Sea by Arnold Colom of Amsterdam . . . 1656*]. *Signed Arnold Colom. Dated 1656. Plane chart, engraved on paper, size 530 × 620 mm. Double-cartouches, in Dutch. From Arnold Colom's sea atlas* ATLAS OF WERELTS-WATER-DEEL EN DESSELFS ZEECUSTEN. NIEULYX VERMEERDERT DOOR JACOB COLOM. . . . *Amsterdam, Jacob Colom, 1663. Engraved title in Dutch; no text. 15 charts. Folio.*

---

This is a fine example of a Dutch sea chart published at a time when the Netherlands led the world in the production of maps and charts. Both the father, JACOB AERTSZ COLOM (1599 or 1600–73), and his son, ARNOLD COLOM (1624–68), were important Dutch chart-publishers of the first half of the seventeenth century. Little is known about their lives, but Jacob Aertsz came from Dordrecht, whence he moved to Amsterdam and set up in business as printer, bookseller, and chart-maker. His house was named *De Vyerighe Colom* and he gave this name to his most important work, a pilot-guide of the northern, eastern, and western navigation, first published in 1632. Many editions followed, in Dutch, French, and English (*The Fierie Sea-Columne*) between 1633 and 1671, some being prepared by his son, Arnold Colom.

Another important production was his *Atlas of Werelts-Water-Deel . . .*, which first appeared in 1663 and whence this chart comes. Translations into French, Latin, Portuguese, and Spanish were published in 1668–9. The atlas is not an entirely original work, being partly composed of charts copied directly from *De Vyerighe Colom*, of revisions from the same source and of new additions. The number of charts varied considerably—fifteen to twenty-three in 1663, rising to twenty-nine or more in the later editions.

As can be seen from the cartouche to this chart of the North Sea, the original lines were taken by Arnold Colom from his 1656 edition of *De Vyerighe Colom*. The chart itself is interesting in its wealth of soundings and representation of the sandbanks in the southern North Sea, though the shapes of the shoals are somewhat stylised. Note, too, the fineness of the engraving surrounding the title cartouche.

# THE SOVTH PART OF VIRGINIA

this Scale Conteineth 20 English Leagues

Made by Nicholas Comberford
Dwelling neere Ratcliffe Crosse

## XXII

# *North Carolina, Pamlico and Albemarle Sounds*

### Nicholas Comberford

### *c 1657*

### 1 : 1,350,000

THE SOVTH PART OF VIRGINIA. MADE BY NICHOLAS COMBERFORD DWELLING IN RADCLIFFE ANNO 1657. MS *on vellum mounted on two hinged oak boards. Coloured. 376 × 495 mm. Plane projection. North is to the right.*

Illustrated opposite is a sea chart from the Thames school that is unusual in several ways: it is a coastal chart on a comparatively large scale, whereas almost all other surviving examples from that school are small-scale oceanic charts; the sketches of animals, sea-monsters, even a gentleman in a tall hat in a dinghy, are embellishments normally scorned by English hydrographers; and it is not overlaid by the graticule of rhumbs that was normal at the time.

It shows the shallow waters of Pamlico and Albemarle Sounds—the same that Verrazano had mistaken for an ocean in 1524 (Chart V)—and the swampy lands and low islands (such as Roanoke) which had been the scene of Raleigh's unsuccessful plantations of 1585 and 1587. When the chart was drawn, all this was part of Virginia: six years later it became part of King Charles II's new colony of Carolina.

There are no soundings, but sailing directions written on the chart indicate the deep-water channels. Instead of the usual system of rhumbs, there is a square grid of apparently arbitrary dimensions that bear no relation to degrees or leagues. From the sketches of the lion and the bear, and from the legend 'This is a swampy wilderness', one can infer that the mainland was not a very inviting place.

The only building shown is *Batts House* at the head of *Roanoake Sound*. Captain Nathaniel Batts was referred to as 'Governor of Roan-oke' by George Fox, founder of the Society of Friends.

NICHOLAS COMBERFORD (fl 1612–70) was apprenticed as platt-maker in the Drapers' Company to John Daniell between 1612 and 1620. He in turn was master to John Burston, who was master to John Thornton, whose apprentice was Joel Gascoyne—thus master-apprentice relations extending over four generations are represented in this book (see Charts XIX, XXVII, and XXX).

Though Comberford was a prolific hydrographer, very little else is known of him. The only known reference is that of Samuel Pepys, who speaks well of him in his diary for 22 July 1663: 'Thence to my booksellers and find my Waggoners done—the very binding cost me 14s—but they are well done, and so by water to Ratcliffe and there went to speak to Cumberford, the platt-maker. And there saw his manner of working which is very fine and labourious.'

### Bibliography

Cumming, W. P. *The Southeast in Early Maps* (Princeton, 1958), 21–4; also 144–5, item 50 and Plate 32

Latham, R. & Matthews, W. (eds). *The Diary of Samuel Pepys*, IV (1971), 240

Smith (1969)

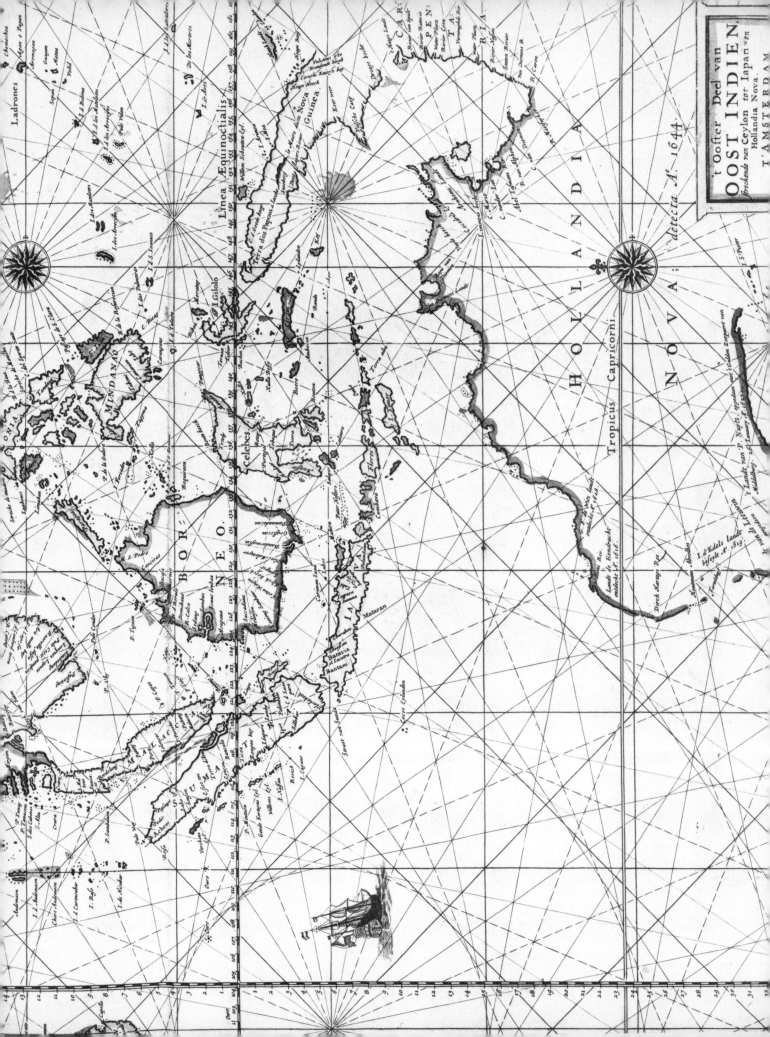

# XXIII

# The East Indies

Hendrick Doncker

*1660*

1 : 15,400,000 (0°)

*Southern half of* T' OOSTER DEEL VAN OOST INDIEN, STRECKENDE VAN CEYLON TOT IAPAN EN HOLLANDIA NOVA. T'AMSTERDAM, BIJ HENDRICK DONCKER BOEKVERKOPER EN GRAADBOOGMAKER IN DE NIEUWBRUGSTEEGH IN'T STUURMANS GERESCHAP. [*The eastern part of the East Indies, from Ceylon to Japan and New Holland [Australia]. By Hendrick Doncker, booksellers and publisher of New Bridge Street, Amsterdam . . .] Signed Hendrick Doncker. Undated. Hand-coloured chart, engraved on paper, size 450 × 565 mm. Plane projection. Single cartouche, in Dutch. From Doncker's sea atlas* DE ZEE-ATLAS OFTE WATER-WAERELD . . . *Amsterdam, Hendrick Doncker, 1661. Dutch text; engraved title; 2 p.l; 24 pp; 26 coloured charts. Folio.*

---

HENDRICK DONCKER (1625 or 1626–99) ran a flourishing business in Nieuwe Brugsteeg, Amsterdam, selling charts and books. In 1655 he began publication of a pilot-guide *Lichtende Columne ofte Zeespiegel,* from which some of the charts were later taken for his sea atlas. Doncker's charts were remarkably original and up-to-date; he took particular pains to correct and improve them and replace obsolete material. His sea atlas *De Zee ofte Water-Waereld . . .* was published in numerous editions (mainly Dutch, but also English, French, and Spanish) between 1660 and 1675, the number of charts gradually increasing from nineteen to thirty. This atlas was followed in 1675 by the magnificent *De Nieuwe Groote Vermeerderde Zee Atlas ofte Waterwerelt,* for which Doncker prepared many new charts in a larger format.

In his 1661 sea atlas Doncker presented the East Indies in two linked charts and the illustration opposite is a detail from the southern half of the second. It is specially interesting for its representation of Australia (*Hollandia Nova*) and the progress of Dutch discoveries on its west and north coasts. Note in particular the entries of *Houtmans Abrolhos, Edelsland, Nuytsland,* and *Dirck Hartogs Ree* on the west and south-west coasts, these being discoveries of Hartog (1616), van Hillegom (1618), de Houtman (1619), Nuyts and Thijssen (1627), Pelsaert (1629), and others. Also of great interest is Doncker's depiction of Carpentaria (Cape York peninsula) and its supposed junction with New Guinea. This charting was derived from the discoveries of Schouten and Le Maire while sailing along the north coast of New Guinea on their voyage round the world (1615–17), and also of Carstens and Colster (1623), but as yet the cartography of the Torres Strait (first navigated by Torres and Prado in 1606) and the stormy Timor Sea was imperfectly known.

Note the Dutch East Indiaman sailing towards the Sunda Strait en route for Batavia (today's Djakarta). It was with ships like these that most of the discoveries on the Australian coast were made, some by chance, when East Indiamen were driven south of their intended tracks (Dirk Hartog in 1616), some by design, in ships sent specially for exploration (Abel Tasman in 1642). This plane chart is unusual in having a longitude scale at a time when few charts did.

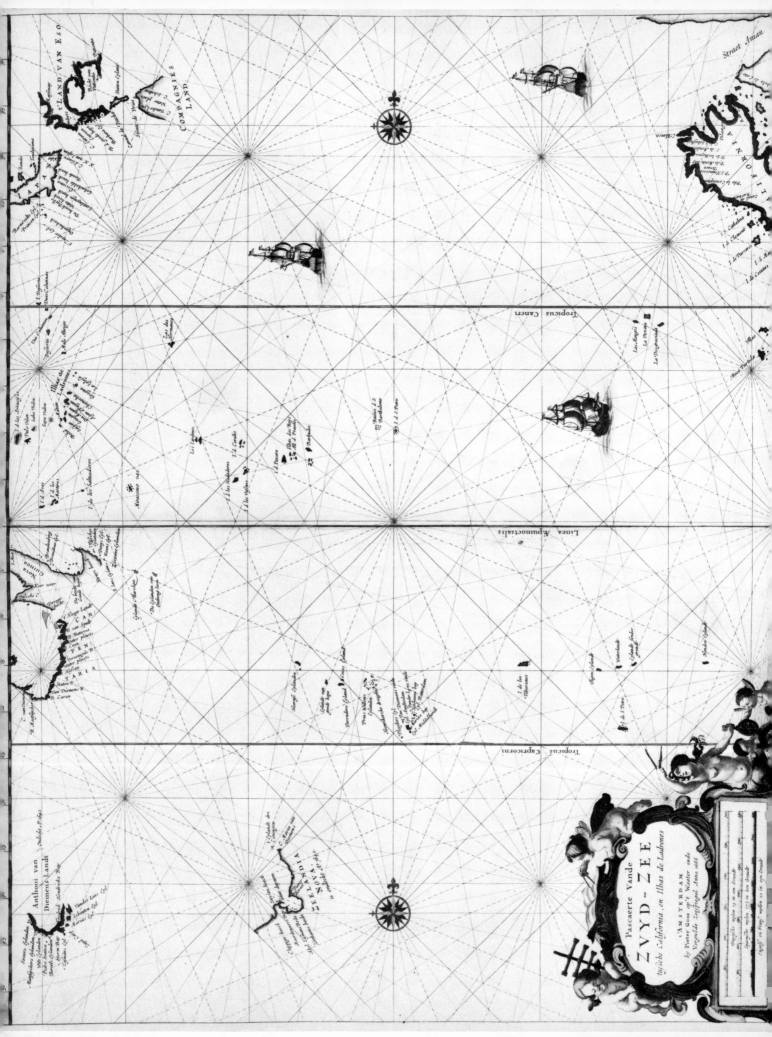

Pascaerte Vande
ZVYD-ZEE
tusschen California, en Ilhas de Ladrones.

t'AMSTERDAM
by Pieter Goos op't Water inde
Vergulde Zeespiegel Anno 1666

# XXIV

# The Pacific Ocean

## Pieter Goos

### 1666

### 1 : 23,000,000

PASCAERTE VANDE ZUYD-ZEE TUSSCHE CALIFORNIA, EN ILHAS DE LADRONES. T'AMSTERDAM BY PIETER GOOS OP'T WAATER INDE VERGULDE ZEESPIEGEL ANNO 1666 [*Chart of the South Seas from California to the Ladrones Islands. By Pieter Goos of Amsterdam . . . 1666*] *Signed Pieter Goos. Dated 1666. Hand-coloured chart, engraved on paper, 440 × 540 mm. Plane chart, north to the right. Single cartouche, in Dutch. From Pieter Goos' sea atlas* De Zee-Atlas ofte Water-Weereld . . . *Amsterdam, Pieter Goos, 1666. Dutch text. Coloured engraved title; [ix] pp, index. 41 coloured charts. Folio.*

---

Whereas manuscript charts such as those of Comberford (Chart XXII) were almost invariably coloured, printed charts were not reproduced in colour until the twentieth century. However, if the customer so wished, chart-sellers were nearly always willing to arrange for printed charts to be hand-coloured before delivery—at extra cost. The atlas from which the chart opposite was taken is a particularly fine example of such hand-colouring.

In the sixteenth and seventeenth centuries, cartouches and title pages frequently included contemporary navigating instruments in their design. Here, the cherubs can be seen holding (left to right) cross-staff, dividers, and mariners' astrolabe.

North is to the right. *Compagnies Land* near Japan was in fact one of the Kurile Islands, mistaken by Maarten Vries in 1642 for a land of continental proportions. *Anthoni van Diemens Landt* and *Zeelandia Nova* are respectively Tasmania and New Zealand, discovered by Abel Tasman in 1642/3. *California* was shown as an island on almost all maps and charts during the seventeenth century, despite the fact that it had been correctly laid down as a peninsula immediately after its discovery (see Chart IX), and this error was not rectified until after Father Kino's journeys (1694-1702). *Straet Anian* just north of California was the western entrance to the mythical but much sought North-west Passage between Atlantic and Pacific, a misconception not finally disproved until Cook's third Pacific voyage of 1776-80 (see also Chart V for the Verrazano Sea with which it was at one time supposed to have been connected).

PIETER GOOS (1616–75), son of the engraver Abraham Goos, established himself as one of the most successful maritime book-sellers in seventeenth-century Amsterdam. He was also a copper engraver and chart-seller, and in 1650 published a pilot-book *Lichtende Columne ofte Zee-Spiegel*, initially with sixty-five charts and later expanded into five parts.

His beautiful *Zee-Atlas* was published in many editions between 1666 and 1683, the first Dutch edition of 1666, from which this chart derives, being followed by versions in English (*The Sea-Atlas or the Watter-World . . ., 1668*), French and Spanish. The contents of the atlases hardly varied—forty to forty-four charts through all their editions—an indication of little incorporation of new material. Indeed, Goos copied many of the charts in Hendrick Doncker's sea atlas, and his atlas is in fact best known for the superb colouring of the cartouches and the engraved title pages. After his death in 1675, the business was carried on by his widow and then by their son, Hendrik Goos.

### Bibliography

Tooley, R. V. 'California as an Island', *Map Collectors' Series*, No 8 (1964)

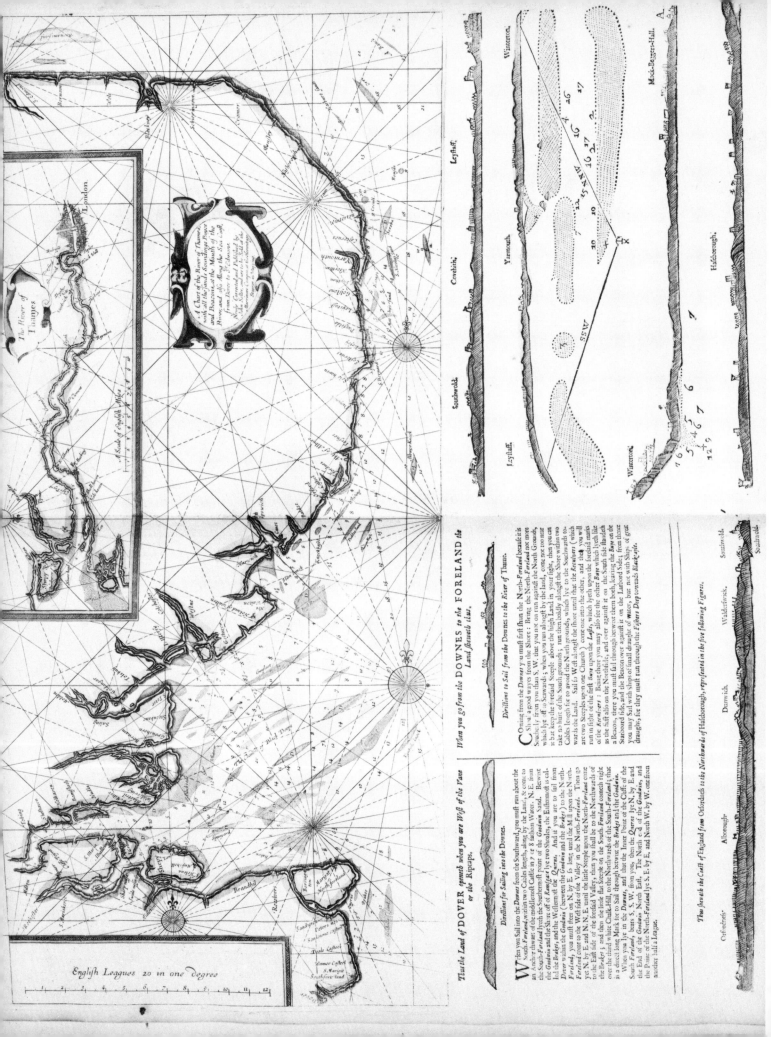

# XXV

# England — East Coast

## John Seller

## [1671]

## 1 : 500,000

A CHART OF THE RIVER OF THAMES, WITH ALL THE SANDS SOUNDING BUYES AND BEACONS, AT THE MOUTH OF THE RIVER, AND ALSO ALONG THE SEA COAST, FROM DOVER TO ST EDMONS. NEWLY CORRECTED AND PUBLISHED BY JOHN SELLER, AND ARE TO BE SOLD AT THE MARRINORS COMPAS, AT THE HERMITAGE STAYRES IN WAPPING. THE RIVER OF THAMES. *Undated. Hand-coloured chart; engraved on paper, 435 × 540 mm. Plane projection. Double-title cartouche; inset cartouche. From John Seller's* THE ENGLISH PILOT . . . LONDON, JOHN DARBY, *1671–2. English text. Two books in one, each with separate printed titles, and Book I also has a coloured engraved title. [xviii] 124 pp; [ii] 80 pp. Folio. 49 coloured charts (26 in Book I; 23 in Book II).*

---

The earliest book of sea charts to be published in England was Joseph Moxon's *Book of Sea Plats* (1657); but this first attempt to compete with the English-language waggoners of Amsterdam and with the manuscript charts of the Thames school of London met with no success. In the late 1660s JOHN SELLER started planning a much more ambitious project, *The English Pilot*, which was eventually to cover the world. Seller (d 1697) was Hydrographer to both Charles II and James II, being granted a monopoly by the former in 1671 for thirty years. He lived for many years at Wapping and had a shop in Exchange Alley, near the Royal Exchange, where he sold his charts and other publications.

A prolific compiler and publisher, his most important work was in the earlier editions of *The English Pilot* series. This major sea-atlas had a long and complicated publishing history from 1671 to 1803, in which Seller and John Thornton played a decisive part at the outset. It was in a sense the first successful English sea-atlas, though Seller obtained much of his material for the charts from earlier Dutch sea-atlases, copying and printing his plates from them. New editions of *The English Pilot* constantly appeared as the work was revised and brought up-to-date. Whatever may have been Seller's intentions and hopes, the end product was adversely criticised by Samuel Pepys and others, particularly for its inaccuracy in charts of home waters. As a result, Captain Greenvile Collins was set to work in 1681 making a survey of Britain's coasts.

The chart illustrated comes from Book I of the first edition of Seller's series, and is one of the charts of the Northern Navigation, that is those embracing Northern Europe. It is an impression from an old Dutch plate and traces of the original Dutch wording can be seen where the title and scale have been re-engraved in English.

Most of the other charts, though completely re-engraved, are from Dutch sources. One, however, is claimed to be entirely English—a new chart of the Thames Estuary, covering the same area as this one, added as an appendix. (It is reproduced in Robinson, Plate 16.) The coastline was taken from a survey by Sir Jonas Moore (1627–79), an important figure in the history of navigation: it was largely through his vision and powers of persuasion that the Royal Observatory was founded at Greenwich in 1675, 'in order to the finding out of the longitude of places for perfecting Navigation and Astronomy' (Royal Warrant dated 22 June 1675).

As with Dutch waggoners, sailing directions formed an integral part of *The English Pilot*. These were printed in letterpress, inset with coastal views. In the chart opposite they are, unusually, on the same page as the engraved chart.

## Bibliography

Tanner, J. R. (ed). 'Samuel Pepys's Naval Minutes', *Navy Records Society*, lx (1926), 19, 42, 238–9, 342–50

Robinson, 37–40

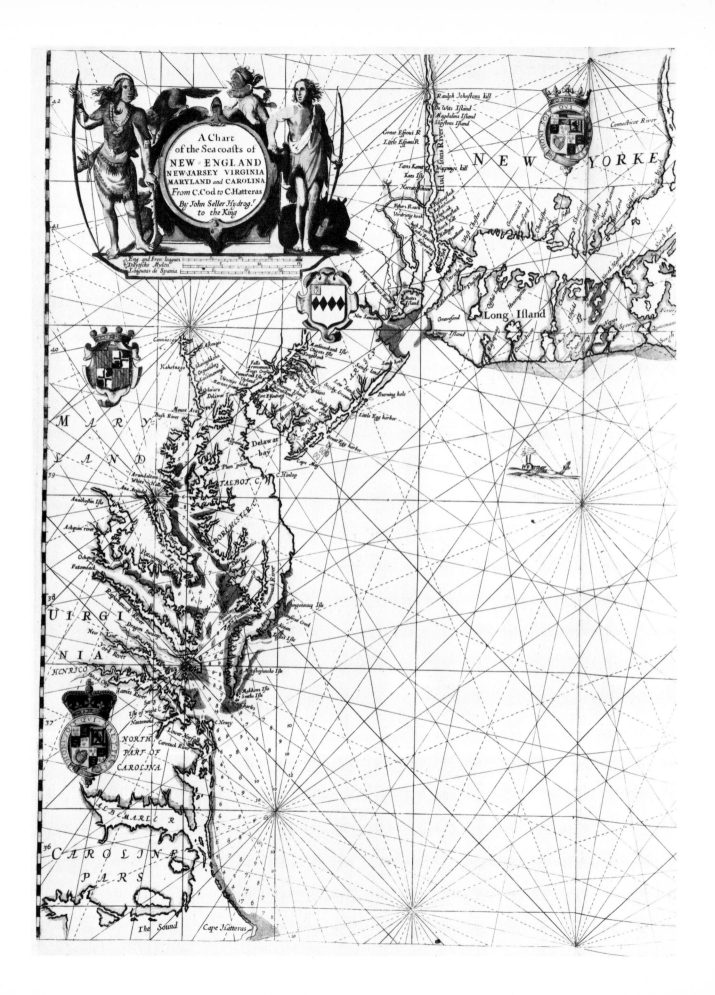

A Chart
of the Sea coasts of
NEW=ENGLAND
NEW-JARSEY VIRGINIA
MARYLAND and CAROLINA
From C.Cod to C.Hatteras
By John Seller Hydrog.r
to the King

Eng. and Fren: leagues
Duytsche Mylen
Leagueas de Spania

NEW YORKE

Connecticot River

Raulph Johnstons kill
De Wits Island
Magdalens Island
Shipstons Island

Great Espous R
Little Espous R

Hudsons River

Wappings kill

Tans Kamt
Kats Isle
Narratschoen

Fishers Reach
Verdrietig hook

Greenwich
Stamford
Norwalk

Milford
Stratford
Fairfield

Long Island

Gravesend
Coney Island

New Sammes

Sandy hook

Little Egg harbor

Burning holz

Great Egg harbor

C. May

Delaware
bay

C. Hinlop

Plum point

TALBOT C.

DORCHESTER

Arundelton
White Hall
Ana Arundel

Anachostin Isle

Achquin river

Ochguis
Patomack

Patomack River

Rapahanock River

Dragon Swamp

New Kent
York River

HENRICO

James River

Isle of wight C.
Nantemsoh

Lower Norf.
Carotuck Isle

NORTH
PART OF
CAROLINA

ALBEMARLE R.

CAROLINÆ
PARS

The Sound        Cape Hatteras

MARY
L
A
N
D

UIRGI
NIA

Cannorogo
Asengo
Kahetnago

Mount Aria
Bush River

40

41

42

39

38

37

36

# XXVI

# The Eastern Seaboard of North America

**John Seller**

*[1675]*

## I : 1,900,000

*Western half of* A CHART OF THE SEA COASTS OF NEW-ENGLAND NEW-JERSEY VIRGINIA MARYLAND AND CAROLINA FROM C. COD TO C. HATTERAS. BY JOHN SELLER HYDROG[r] TO THE KING. *Signed John Seller and the engraver James Clerk. Hand-coloured chart engraved on paper, 435 × 540 mm. Plane projection. Title and dedicatory cartouches (text of second blank). From Seller's* ATLAS MARITIMUS. *London, John Darby, 1675. English text. Coloured engraved title; printed title; (iv), 16 pp Folio. 30 coloured charts.*

---

As we have just seen, Seller was forced on occasion to use old Dutch plates for some of his charts, but generally he was able to have them re-engraved in England, as in this case. In describing his bar-scales in the three appropriate languages he was presumably thinking of his export market.

In contrast to the more ambitious and complex *The English Pilot* series, John Seller's *Atlas Maritimus* was published as a single volume sea-atlas. There were several editions after 1675, most of them undated, and the contents differ. It appears that the atlases were prepared to meet individual requirements. A very similar *Atlas Maritimus* was published by Seller's colleague John Thornton, and a later work, the *Atlas Maritimus Novus*, appeared in 1708, 1750, and 1755 under the auspices of Mount & Page.

Seller's *Atlas Maritimus* of 1675 is not very original, for he, and Thornton, relied heavily on earlier Dutch material, and it is known that in 1669–70 he copied many of the charts in Pieter Goos' *Zee-Atlas*.

Features of the atlas are the magnificent cartouches, superb colouring, and general decorative effect, of which this chart is a good example. The bottom left-hand corner shows the same area as did Comberford in his manuscript chart (XXII). Between the dates of these two charts, 1657 and 1675, the colony of Carolina had been founded, and named after Charles II, in 1663.

This is a plane chart. Until the end of the eighteenth century, hydrographers generally used Mercator's projection only for ocean and world charts.

NOVA FRANCE

Cannada

NOVA ANGLIA

New Jarze

MARY=LAND

VIRGINIA

Carolina

FLORIDA

MEX
I
CO

Tascala

Guaxica

Tabasco

Honduras

Nicorago

Varagua

Cartagena

HISPANIOA

TRO

MARE

oronoco

# XXVII

# West Indies and Gulf of Mexico

Joel Gascoyne
*1678*

## I : 10,100,000

*No title. Detail from Western half of chart of Atlantic, signed* MADE BY JOEL GASCOYNE AT Yᵉ SIGN OF THE PLATT AT WAPING OLD STAYRES ANᵒ: DOM: 1678. FOR CAP:ᵗ JOHN SMITH. *Hand-coloured* MS *chart, mounted on two hinged oak boards, 711 × 533 mm. Plane projection.*

---

Illustrated opposite is a detail from a hand-drawn chart of the North Atlantic produced in London by a member of the Thames school. Only half has survived but the original would have covered the whole ocean between Europe and America and would have been mounted on four hinged oak boards. The two surviving boards cover the western ocean. They carry the signature of the cartographer, Joel Gascoyne, and, on the back of one of them, written in ink, the name 'Cap. John Smyth', the man for whom the chart was made. Nothing is known of this Captain John Smyth (or Smith), for he was not the famous Captain John Smith—American colonist, soldier, sailor, writer, author of the first English dictionary of the sea, *The Seaman's Grammar* (1627)—who had died in 1631.

Three very similar Thames-school charts of the Atlantic are preserved at Greenwich—one of 1650 by Nicholas Comberford, one of 1674 by Andrew Welch, and this half-chart of 1678 by Joel Gascoyne. They must have had a common ancestor, for all are exactly to the same scale (about 1 in 10 million), the same size in their original state, and have their illuminated compass roses and bar-scales in the same relative positions. There are, however, many differences in detail, notably in the trend of the coastline of South Carolina and Georgia (not at that time so named). In the two earliest charts it runs almost EW, whereas, in Gascoyne's chart reproduced here, the trend of the coast between St Augustine and Cape Fear is NNE, which is almost correct. There are differences also in the soundings south of Newfoundland and Nova Scotia.

JOEL GASCOYNE (d 1706) was apprenticed to John Thornton, platt-maker in the Drapers' Company, between 1668 and 1675 (see Chart XXX). Four manuscript charts, dated between 1678 and 1693, and a few printed charts signed by him either as engraver (see Chart XXX) or as hydrographer, are known (see Charts XIV, XVII, XXV). He was also an estate surveyor and drew other land maps, particularly of Cornwall.

In 1682, he published *A New Map of the Country of Carolina*, known as the second Lords Proprietors' Map. This was both map and chart, having on the one hand full land details with settlements, flora and fauna, and on the other, ample soundings and a compass rose.

Samuel Pepys consulted Gascoyne in connection with his investigations into the state of English hydrography—investigations which resulted in the publication of Collins's *Great Britain's Coasting Pilot* (Chart XXXI).

In October 1680, Pepys minuted: 'Get Gascoin the platmaker to compare the original and later Waggoners with Anthony Ashley's and Seller's new maps.'

## Bibliography

Cumming, W. P. *The Southeast in Early Maps* (Princeton, 1958), 159–60 and Plate 39

Ravenhill, W. 'Joel Gascoyne—a cartographer with style', *Geographical Magazine* (February 1972), 335–41

Smith, (1969)

Tanner, J. R. (ed). 'Samuel Pepys's Naval Minutes', *Navy Records Society*, lx (1926), 42

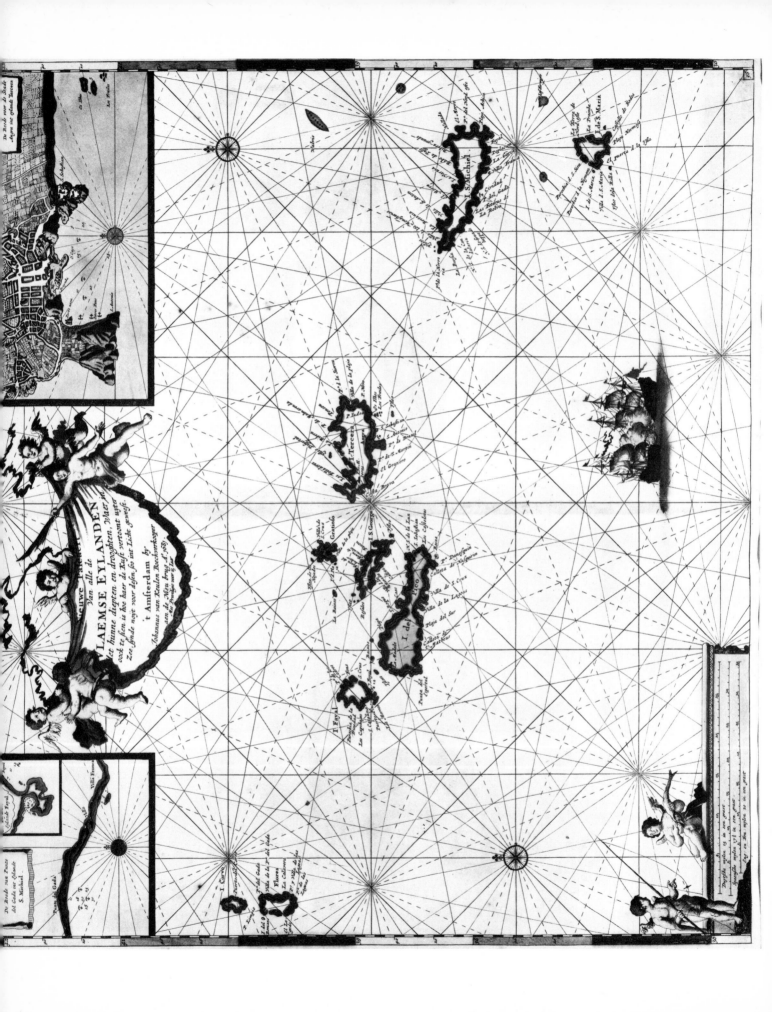

# XXVIII

# The Azores (The Flemish Islands)

**Johannes Van Keulen, *The Elder***

*1681*

## 1 : 1,460,000

NIEUWE PASCAERT VAN ALLE DE VLAEMSE EYLANDEN . . . 'T AMSTERDAM BY JOHANNES VAN KEULEN BOECKVERKOOPER AEN DE NIEU BRUG Aᵒ. 1681. MET PREVILIGIE VOOR 15 IAAR.

INSETS (1) DE REEDE VOOR DE STADT ANGRA INT EYLANDT TERCERA

(2) DE REEDE VAN PUNTE DEL GADA INT EYLANDT S. MICHIEL

(3) DE ZUYDHOEC VANT EYLANDT FAYAL

*[New chart of all the Flemish Islands [the Azores] . . . by Johannes Van Keulen, book-seller of Amsterdam . . . 1681. . . . ] Signed Johannes Van Keulen. Dated 1681. Coloured chart, engraved on paper, size 505 × 580 mm. Plane projection. Single cartouche, in Dutch. From Johannes Van Keulen's sea atlas* THE GREAT AND NEWLY ENLARGED SEA ATLAS OR WATERWORLD *. . . Amsterdam, Johannes Van Keulen, 1682. English prefatory text and index; coloured engraved title in English. 143 coloured charts. Folio.*

---

JOHANNES VAN KEULEN (born at Deventer 1654, died in Amsterdam 1715) founded the publishing house that produced some of the first and largest marine atlases in Holland. An important factor in the development of the firm was the acquisition of the stock of the chart-publisher and bookseller Hendrick Doncker (see Chart XXIII). Later Van Keulen's son Gerard, grandson Johannes and great-grandson Gerard Hulst continued the business.

The two most important productions of the Van Keulens were the *Zee-Fakkel* (which originally appeared as the five-volume *Nieuwe groote ligtende Zee-Fakkel* in 1681–4 in association with Claes Jansz-Vooght) and the *Zee-Atlas*. The latter had a long and complex history, beginning with forty charts in the Dutch edition of 1680 and gradually expanding to a peak of 185 charts.

The chart illustrated comes from a rare English edition of the *Zee-Atlas*; the title is dated 1682 but the large number of charts indicates the inclusion of later material. In Van Keulen's day the Azores were known as the Flemish Islands because in 1466 the island of Fayal had been given to Isabella of Burgundy as part of a treaty settlement; later the whole group of islands came under Portuguese and then Spanish control. Note in Van Keulen's chart a number of inserts to depict local anchorages and harbours and the fine quality of the pictorial illustrations.

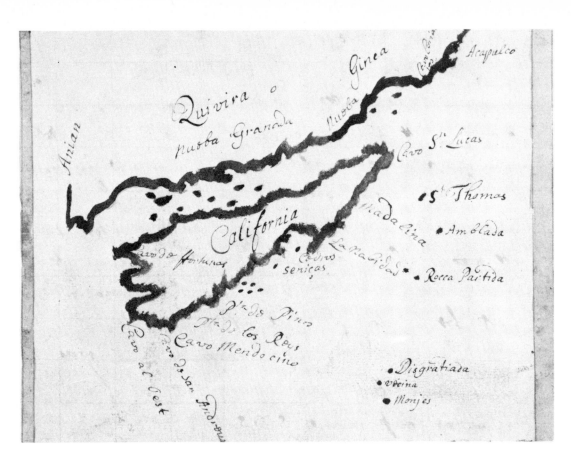

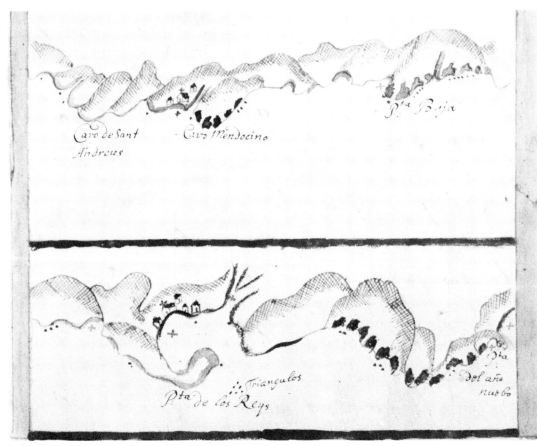

# XXIX

# California

**Basil Ringrose**

*c 1682–3*

*(a) California, general —*

approx 1 : 27,000,000

*(b) Cape Mendocino vicinity —*

approx 1 : 2,000,000

*(c) San Francisco Bay vicinity —*

approx 1 : 1,000,000

MS *on paper. Pen and ink and wash.* (a) *147 × 187 mm to edge of border ;* (b) *and* (c) *147 × 184 mm. Plane projection. Folios 2r and 3r from the* MS *book* THE SOUTH SEA WAGGONER SHEWING THE MAKING AND BEARING OF ALL THE COASTS FROM CALIFORNIA TO THE STRIEGHTS OF LE MAIRE DONE FROM THE SPANISH ORIGINALL BY BASIL RINGROSE.

---

When the charts opposite were drawn, California was unexplored, the nearest Spanish settlement being Acapulco in Mexico, many miles to the south. The charts are interesting not only in themselves in showing what was known, and what was believed, of California at this time, but also because they come from a unique 'South Sea Waggoner', compiled by an English buccaneer, using information from captured Spanish documents.

BASIL RINGROSE was a member of the crew of the English buccaneer ship *Trinity*, commanded by Captain Bartholomew Sharpe in the Pacific and Caribbean. On 29 July 1681 the *Trinity*, herself a Spanish prize, captured the Spanish *Rosario* off the coast of modern Ecuador. Among the prizes taken that day was a book of sea charts and sailing directions for the Pacific coast from Acapulco to Cape Horn, compiled in Panama in 1669, 'which serveth them [the Spaniards] for a complete Wagenaer'.

Sharpe, realising the strategic value to England of this information on coasts considered by Spain as her private preserves, had the text translated by a Jewish friend, Phillip Dassigny, and the charts copied by William Hack, platt-maker of Wapping. The resulting manuscript, *Waggoner of the Great South Sea*, was presented to Charles II in 1682, in which year also Sharpe and four others (not Ringrose) stood trial in London on charges of piracy and the murder of Don Diego Lopez of the *Rosario*. Their acquittal on the grounds of self-defence was said to have been helped by Sharpe's presentation of his manuscript.

Fourteen manuscript copies of the Sharpe/Hack *Waggoner* and its derivatives are known (including one at Greenwich dedicated to James II), but this copy of Ringrose's *South Sea Waggoner* seems to be unique. Though less elegant than Hack's highly coloured products, Ringrose's book contains far more information—there is a very full text, soundings on many of the charts, and a description of Upper and Lower California 'from the Originall of Don Melchor' that does not appear in Hack.

Ringrose's journal of the voyage was published as Volume II of the *Buccaneers of America* (Esquemeling) in 1685. He was killed in a skirmish with the Spaniards in Mexico in 1686, during a voyage in which William Dampier took part.

The top chart shows the whole of California, demonstrating the two seventeenth-century cartographic misconceptions already mentioned—the 'Strait of Anian' and California as an island. The other two charts show the coast from *Cavo de Sant Andreus*, 'gross cloudy land very high' (not identified for certain), somewhere north of *C. Mendocino* (40° 26′ N), past Point Reyes, the Farallon Islands (*Triangulos*), and the entrance to San Francisco Bay (not discovered until 1769), to Point Año Nuovo (37° 7′ N, just north of Monterey).

Of the San Francisco area, Ringrose writes as follows:

Hence the coast runnes SEbs till you come at *P*^ta *de los Reys* an Endiferent pointe in heighte: at some distance it seemes an Island and when it is a rounde hill. It is an excellent port and you are here safe from all winds: in the harbour you have a Creeke in w^ch is safe and smooth riding and find friendly Indians and good watering: the Coast is shoaly soe keep 5 or 6 leagues offe and when you see *los Triangulos* then make in for the porte: here was lost the Ship St. Augustine 1595 by sailing too near the pointe.

Ringrose uses the symbol + to mark anchorages. The one NW of Pt. Reyes is probably today's Bodega Bay. The one inside the point is certainly Drake's Bay. The next anchorage down the coast might seem to be in the entrance to San Francisco Bay, but this is unlikely in view of the strength of the tidal stream in the Golden Gate, and it probably represents Drake's Estero, an inlet in Drake's Bay. (Whether or not Drake's Bay and Drake's Estero—so called on today's maps—were seen by Sir Francis Drake himself is still the subject of controversy among scholars.)

## Bibliography

Esquemeling, J. *The Buccaneers of America . . . translation of 1684–5* (Broadway Translations, 1924), 278

John Carter Brown Library *Annual Report* for 1965–6

Kemp, P. K., & Lloyd, C. *The Brethren of the Coast* (1960)

Lloyd, C. C. 'Bartholomew Sharp, Buccaneer', *The Mariners' Mirror*, vol 42 (1956), 291–301

Lynham, Edward. *The Mapmaker's Art* (1953), 101–16

Wagner, Henry R. *The Cartography of the Northwest Coast of America . . .*, 2 vols (Berkeley, 1937, reprinted Amsterdam, 1968). Wagner does not record Ringrose's Waggoner

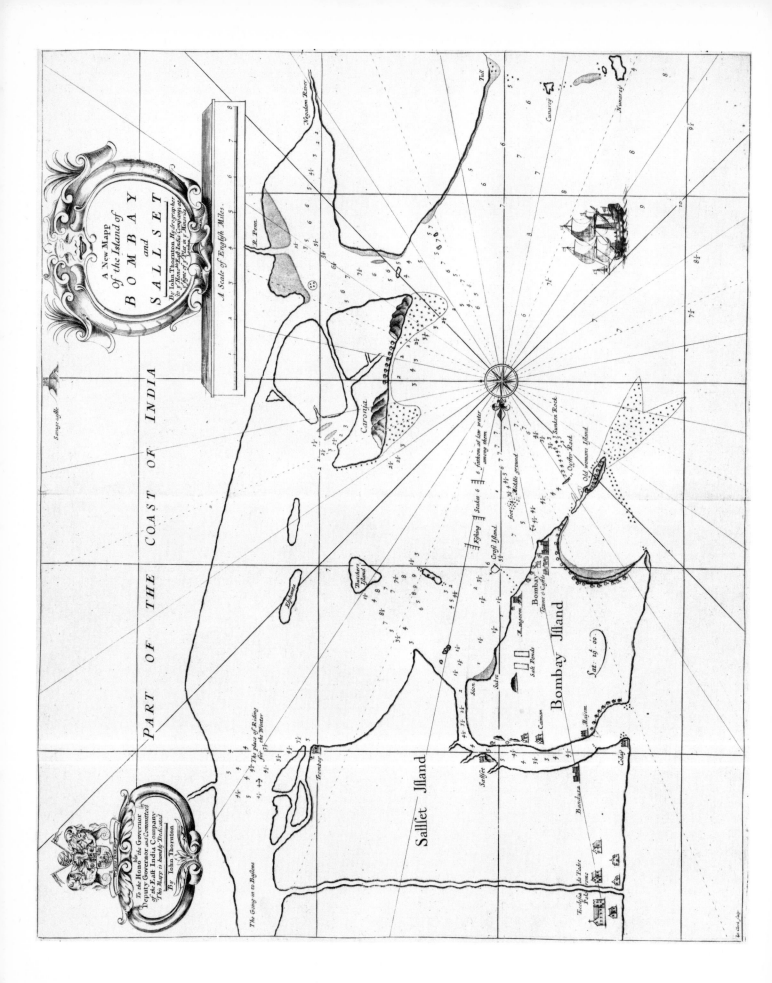

ors and Committee of the East India Company. The material is clearly presented—note the soundings off Bombay, and the fishing stakes and the winter anchorage in the Bassein estuary.

# Bombay

**John Thornton**

*c 1685*

1 : 78,000

A NEW MAPP OF THE ISLAND OF BOMBAY AND SALLSET. BY IOHN THORNTON HYDROGRAPHER TO YE HONRBLE EAST INDIA COMPANY; AT YE SIGNE OF YE PLAT IN YE MINORIES LONDON. *Signed John Thornton and the engraver James Clerk* [Ia: Clerk sculp:]. *Undated. Uncoloured chart, engraved on paper, 435 × 530 mm. Plane projection. Title and dedicatory cartouches; [scale in English miles]. From John Thornton's* ATLAS MARITIMUS: OR THE SEA-ATLAS . . . *London, John Thornton, [c 1685]. English text; engraved title; pp [1]-10; [1]-16. Folio. 58 uncoloured charts.*

---

Unlike so many charts published in England at this time, this chart by the East India Company's hydrographer may well have been based on an English survey. Bombay had recently become the chief of the East India Company's possessions in India, having been ceded to Britain by Portugal in 1661 as part of the dowry of the Infanta Catharine of Braganza on her marriage to Charles II. In 1668 Bombay was transferred to the East India Company for an annual payment of £10.

JOHN THORNTON (fl 1656–1706) collaborated with John Seller in many of his publications, but was also an hydrographer in his own right, at one time under such appointment with the East India Company.

He was a member of the Thames school, having been apprenticed to John Burston of the Drapers' Company in 1656 (see Chart XIX), and Joel Gascoyne was apprenticed to him in 1668 (see Chart XXVII). Like his colleagues, Thornton produced manuscript charts drawn on vellum and mounted on wooden boards, similar to Charts XIX, XXII, and XXVII. He was, however, the only member of that school to publish *printed* charts in any numbers, though his pupil Joel Gascoyne was the engraver of the English channel chart in the same atlas.

As a skilled engraver, he was commissioned to execute Narbrough's chart of the South Seas, published in 1673. He played an important part in the production of the various editions of Seller's *Atlas Maritimus*, and later issued his own version, from which this chart comes. Most of the charts in the atlas are the combined work of Thornton, Seller, Fisher, Colson, and Atkinson.

This copy of the atlas is of added interest for the owner's contemporary inscription on the flyleaf: 'Reginald Graham Esq. page of honour to King James the Second: his Booke; given to him by King James the Second: Anno Domini 1687'.

John Thornton dedicated his chart of Bombay to the Govern-

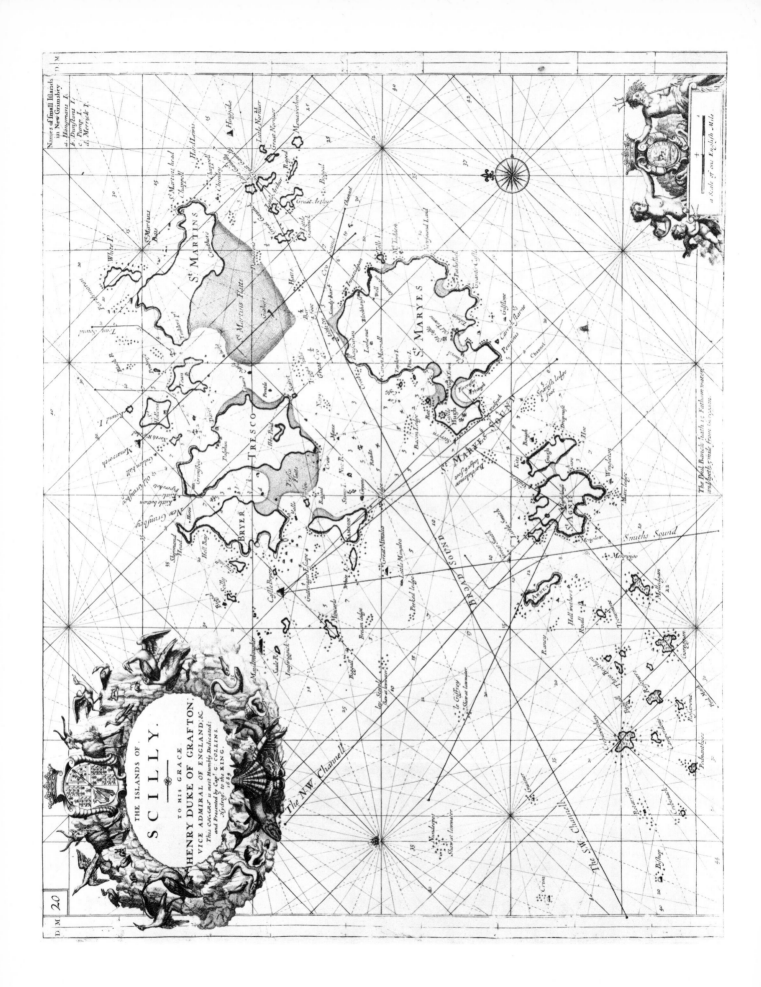

# XXXI

# The Scilly Islands

## Captain Greenvile Collins

### 1689

### 1 : 37,500

THE ISLANDS OF SCILLY. TO HIS GRACE HENRY DUKE OF GRAFTON; VICE ADMIRAL OF ENGLAND &C. THIS IS MOST HUMBLY DEDICATED AND PRESENTED BY CAP^T. G. COLLINS. HYDROG^r. TO THE KING. *1689. Signed Greenvile Collins. Dated 1689. Uncoloured chart, engraved on paper, 450 × 560 mm. Plane projection. Title and scale cartouches. From Greenvile Collins' atlas* GREAT BRITAIN'S COASTING-PILOT. THE FIRST PART . . . THE SECOND PART . . . *London, Freeman Collins & Richard Mount, 1693. English text. Engraved title; printed titles to both parts, in black and red; [xii], 22 pp; 28 pp Folio. 48 uncoloured charts (28 in part I, 20 in part II).*

---

One of the results of the criticism levelled at Seller's charts (see Chart XXV) was that the Admiralty began to realise just how little original surveying had been carried out in British waters in the seventeenth century. Samuel Pepys, writing in 1682, could discover only five such surveys. He goes on: 'Seller's maps are at best but copies of the Dutch, with such improvements as he could make therein by private advice upon the observations of single men . . . Captain Collins says, and did upon view by comparing the maps, shew me by several instances that our sea-coasts were better laid down by Speed than they are in our Waggoner'.

To rectify this state of affairs, Captain Greenvile Collins was in 1681 commissioned by the Admiralty (supported by a somewhat reluctant Trinity House), to carry out a complete survey of all the sea coasts of Great Britain. As a young man Collins had accompanied Narbrough on his voyage to the South Seas, 1669–71, and was later master of Narbrough's flagship, the *Plymouth*. In 1681 he became a Younger Brother of Trinity House and was then commissioned by the Admiralty to undertake the survey of the coasts of Great Britain.

Progress in this immense task was slow, partly through lack of money, but by 1688 Collins and his assistants had prepared 120 plans of harbours and stretches of open coast. Only 48 of these were finally engraved and used in the atlas, first published in 1693, *Great Britain's Coasting Pilot* . . . Despite many inaccuracies, the work is a landmark in British hydrography, being the first complete pilot-book in English of the entire British coast, including Orkney, Shetland, and the Scilly Islands. Following the original publication in 1693, no less than fourteen editions appeared between 1723 and 1792, with remarkably little change of content. This chart of the Scilly Islands is a good example of Collins' cartographic style. A particular feature is the marking of leading and clearing lines: for example, the island of Great Smith kept in line with Castle Bryer will lead through Smith's Sound, west of St Agnes.

For some reason, the figures giving degrees and minutes on the latitude graduation have been expunged on this plate.

## Bibliography

Robinson, 40–3

Tanner, J. R. (ed). 'Samuel Pepys's Naval Minutes', *Navy Records Society*, lx (1926), 135–6

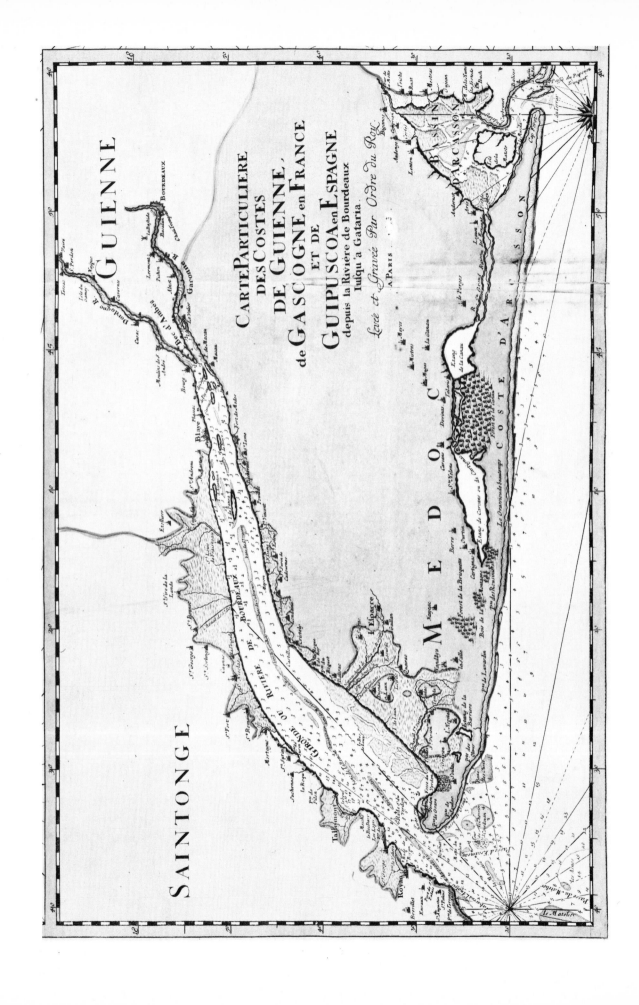

SAINTONGE

GUIENNE

CARTE PARTICULIERE
DES COSTES
DE GUIENNE,
de GASCOGNE en FRANCE,
ET DE
GUIPUSCOA en ESPAGNE
depuis la Riviere de Bourdeaux
Iusqu'a Gataria.

Levée et Gravée Par Ordre du Roy.

A PARIS.

BOURDEAUX

RIVIERE DE BOURDEAUX OU GIRONDE

MTs DE MEDOC

COSTE D'ARCASSON

BASSIN D'ARCASSON

# XXXII

# Gironde Estuary and River

## Alexis Hubert Jaillot & Pierre Mortier

## [1693]

## 1 : 217,000

*Inset from* CARTE PARTICULIERE DES COSTES DE GUIENNE, DE GASCOGNE EN FRANCE ET DE GUIPUSCOA EN ESPAGNE DEPUIS LA RIVIÈRE DE BOURDEAUX IUSQU'A GATARIA. LEVÉE ET GRAVÉE PAR ORDRE DU ROY. A PARIS. 1693, *with inset on same scale:* [*Gironde ou Rivière de Bourdeaux*]. *'Special chart of the coasts of Guyenne, Gascony in France and Guipuzcoa in Spain, from the Gironde estuary to Gataria. Drawn and engraved by royal command. Paris. 1693.' Unsigned. Dated 1693. Coloured chart, engraved on paper, 580 × 820 mm. Mercator's projection. North is to the left. From Jaillot's sea atlas* LE NEPTUNE FRANÇOIS, OU ATLAS NOUVEAU DES CARTES MARINES . . . *French text. Engraved and printed titles, both coloured; 6 pp; table of contents; scale-chart; large Folio. 38 coloured charts.*

---

On 27 December 1691 Louis XIV granted *Ingénieur et géographe* Charles Péne leave to publish an atlas of twenty-nine charts and six pages of text, to be called *Le Neptune François*. This was duly published with the imprint: *Paris, Imprimerie Royale, 1693*. Though under official auspices, the actual publication seems to have been done privately.

The charts, engraved on Mercator's projection by H. van Loon and C. Berey, were based on surveys by various *ingénieurs du roy*, initiated by the Minister, Colbert, in 1666. According to J. N. Bellin, the main authors were Saveur and de Chazelles. Péne acted as editor. Other *ingénieurs* who contributed were de la Voye, Duchon, Sabran, Razaut, de la Favolière, Minet, and de Gennes. Volume I covered the Atlantic coasts of Europe; Volume II, though announced in Volume I as covering the Mediterranean, did not appear until many years later.

Thus, thanks to Colbert's initiative, France's *armées de mer* had official charts, based on official surveys, over 100 years before their British counterparts, though Bellin says somewhat ruefully that the Navy did not appreciate them as they ought to have done.

But the Dutch, then the leading publishers of sea charts, were not to be outdone. In the same year, Pierre Mortier of Amsterdam, in partnership with Hubert Jaillot of Paris, had all the plates very precisely re-engraved, with the French engravers' names omitted but the words '*Levées et Gravées Par Ordre du Roy*' added to the titles. Three versions of this counterfeit edition—for counterfeit it was—were published simultaneously in Amsterdam with French, Dutch, and English texts— (a) *Le Neptune François . . . Paris, 1693* (though actually printed in Amsterdam, the name Paris was put on the title page 'to promote sales'); (b) *De Fransche Neptunus . . . Amsterdam, P. Mortier, 1693;* and (c) *The French Neptune . . . Amsterdam, P. Mortier, 1693*.

The subsequent history of the French edition will be found under Chart XLIII.

The chart opposite is taken from a copy of the Dutch edition with a French text. With the exception of the minor differences mentioned above, it is identical with the original French chart.

ALEXIS HUBERT JAILLOT (c 1632–1712) followed the Sansons in maintaining the pre-eminence of the French school of cartography in the late seventeenth century. Originally a sculptor, he became interested in cartography after his marriage to the daughter of Nicolas Berey, the famous map-colourist. After working in collaboration with Guillaume and Adrien Sanson, Jaillot had by 1680 established his own reputation.

His most important productions were the *Atlas Nouveau* (first published in 1681, with forty-five maps); the *Atlas François* (1695, forty-five maps), and the sumptuous *Le Neptune François . . .* (1693), a seminal work in the development of the French sea atlas. An attractive feature of the Dutch *Le Neptune François* was the simultaneous publication in 1693 of a supplementary volume consisting of a series of beautifully engraved plates of sailing ships and national flags.

## Bibliography

Anon. 'Notice sur le Service Hydrographique de la Marine', *Annales hydrographiques, 1914* (Paris, 1914), 7

Bellin, J. N. 'Remarques sur les cartes du Neptune François dont les Planches ont été remises au Dépôt des Plans de la Marine en 1753', *Le Neptune François . . . Premier Volume* (Paris, 1753), Preface

Koeman, IV, 423–4

# A NEW CHART
### OF THE
# CHANNELL
*Between*
# ENGLAND
### AND
# FRANCE

*English and French Leagues*

*Sold by Richard Mount and Thomas Page at the Postern on Great Tower Hill London.*

## ADVERTISMENT

In this **Channell Draught**, *the smaller figures are the depth in fathoms. The Litterall or Roman figures shew the hour of* **Highwater**, *or rather the end of the stream that sets to the Eastwards, on the day of the* **New & Full Moon**. *Add therefore the time of the Moon Southing or Northing to the Number found near the place where your Shipp is, and the Summe shall show you how long the Tyde will run to the Eastwards. but if it be more then 12 Subtract 12 therefrom. The Direction of the Darts shew upon what point of the Compaß the strength of the Tyde Setts.*

# *The English Channel*

## After Edmond Halley

*c 1702*

1 : 1,150,000

A NEW CHART OF THE CHANNELL BETWEEN ENGLAND AND FRANCE. SOLD BY RICHARD MOUNT AND THOMAS PAGE AT THE POSTERN ON GREAT TOWER HILL LONDON. *Signed Richard Mount & Thomas Page. Undated. Uncoloured chart, engraved on paper, 450 × 570 mm. Plane projection. Title and 'Advertisement' panel. From Richard Mount & Thomas Page's sea atlas* ATLAS MARITIMUS NOVUS, OR THE NEW SEA-ATLAS . . . *London, Richard Mount & Thomas Page, 1702. English text; printed title, in red and black; 8 pp, Folio. 39 uncoloured charts.*

---

This important chart is the direct result of Edmond Halley's third voyage in the *Paramore* pink. (The spelling of the ship's name is that adopted by Halley himself.) Between June and October 1701 Halley carried out a remarkable survey of the tidal streams and magnetic variation in the whole English Channel, as well as fixing the positions of the Ripraps, Owers, and Bramble shoals, the Casquet Rocks, and the island of Alderney. For most of the voyage he had on board Peter St Croix, a pilot from St Aubin, Jersey.

HALLEY (1656–1742) was already a distinguished scientist—though he would have called himself a natural philosopher—when he undertook his two earlier voyages in the *Paramore* (1698–1700) to obtain data on magnetic variation in the Atlantic —the first purely scientific voyages ever made. He published his results in a magnetic chart of the Atlantic in 1702, followed a year later by a similar chart of the world. In 1714 Halley became one of the first commissioners of the newly formed Board of Longitude, and in 1721, at the age of sixty-five, succeeded Flamsteed as Astronomer Royal at Greenwich, a post he held until his death in 1742.

Though the chart reproduced here is usually attributed to Halley, he, in fact, supplied only the magnetic and tidal data. A similar chart, unlike this one in actually mentioning Halley's name in the title, was published by John Thornton in his *The English Pilot, The Third Book* of 1703. Larger versions in sheet form were published a few years later both by Mount & Page and by Samuel Thornton (John's son), and various undated editions of both sizes were extant for the next sixty years or so. The best way of dating the various editions is by noting the amount of the magnetic variation given.

The method of showing the tidal information was novel, though it has been used many times since. The Roman figures show the hours of High Water (which, according to Halley, is also the time of the end of the east-going stream) on the days of New and Full Moon. The advertisement gives instructions for finding the time of the tide turning on other days of the month.

The publishing house of Mount & Page was closely connected with the production of the later editions of the important *The English Pilot* series, first begun by John Seller and John Thornton. Indeed, the majority of the charts in the *Atlas Maritimus Novus* are very similar to those from Seller and Thornton. Later editions of the Mount & Page atlas were published in 1708, 1750 and 1755.

## Bibliography

Halley, Edmond. 'A Journall of a Voiage in his Ma[ties] Pink The Paramore: for discovery of the Course of the Tides in The Channell of England. By Edmond Halley Commander. Anno 1701', British Museum Additional MSS 30368, ff 37–47, in Halley's own hand and signed. Folios 1 to 36 are a copy of Halley's journal of his first two voyages, written by an amanuensis

Proudman, J. 'Halley's tidal chart', *Geographical Journal*, XCIX (1942), 174–6

Thrower, N. J. W. 'Edmond Halley as a thematic geo-cartographer', *Annals of the Association of American Geographers*, LIX, No 4 (December 1969), 652–76

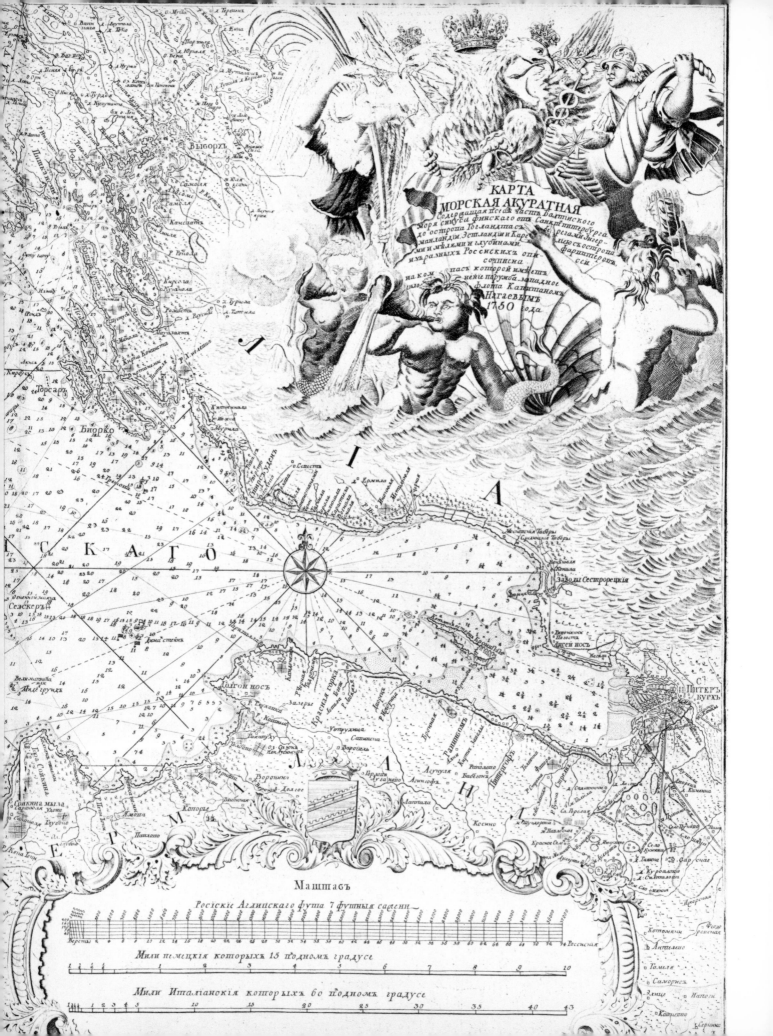

necessary in coastal waters. The bar-scales show the contemporary confusion in measurement, with Russian fathoms, English feet, and German and Italian miles.

Minor mistakes in language indicate that the engraver of this chart could well have been a foreigner, and the style is reminiscent of Dutch charts of some years earlier. In building the Imperial Russian Navy, Peter the Great had imported experts from both Britain and the Netherlands.

# The Gulf of Finland

**Alexei Nagaev**

*1750*

**I : 325,000**

*Eastern half of* КАРТА МОРСКАЯ АКУРАТНАЯ . . . 1750 [AN ACCURATE SEA CHART CONTAINING THE GULF OF FINLAND, PART OF THE BALTIC SEA FROM ST PETERSBURG TO THE ISLAND OF GOGLAND FROM THE SHORES OF INGERMANLAND, ESTLAND, AND KARELIA WITH THE ISLANDS AND SHALLOWS AND DEPTHS OF THE FAIRWAYS TAKEN FROM VARIOUS RUSSIAN SURVEYS AND COMPILED . . . BY CAPTAIN OF THE FLEET NAGAEV, 1750]. *Signed Nagaev. Dated 1750. Plane chart, engraved on paper, 550 × 735 mm. Single cartouche in Cyrillic script. Three bar-scales: 'Russian fathoms of 7 English feet to each; German miles of which there are 15 to each degree; Italian miles of which there are 60 to each degree [ie nautical miles]'. From Nagaev's sea-atlas:* Атласъ всего Ъалтiйскаго моря . . . Флота капитаномъ перьваго ранга Алексѣемъ Нагаевымъ. ATLAS OF THE WHOLE BALTIC SEA WITH THE GULFS OF FINLAND AND BOTHNIA, THE SKAGGERAK AND KATTEGAT, THE SOUND AND THE BELTS . . .] *Moscow, 1794. Printed title; no text; index of contents. Folio. 24 sea charts.*

---

This Russian chart was published in the reign of the Empress Elizabeth (1709–62), daughter of Peter the Great (1672–1725), the virtual founder of the Russian Navy. It was an official publication, based on Russian surveys, and engraved and printed in the Printing House of the Naval Cadet College in the then Russian capital, St Petersburg (now Leningrad)—founded by Peter in 1703 where the River Neva debouched into the Gulf of Finland, seen here on the right.

Commanding the sea approaches to the capital is the island of Kronstadt, where Peter founded a naval base and fortress in 1710. The gulf at top left leads up to the port of Vyborg. All these ports are closed by ice from November to April, as indeed is the greater part of the Gulf.

Technically the chart is excellent, with clear soundings (presumably in Russian fathoms of 7 English ft) and rather more land detail than was usual at that time. Note the St Petersburg streets on the left bank of the Neva, radiating out from the old Admiralty building; and the road along the south shore between the city and Peter's great summer palace, the Peterhof.

Two examples of shoals marked by floating beacons can be seen, one sw of, and close to, Kronstadt, and one near the left edge of the illustration: such buoys would have been removed each winter before the formation of sea ice.

There is no latitude and longitude graduation but that is not

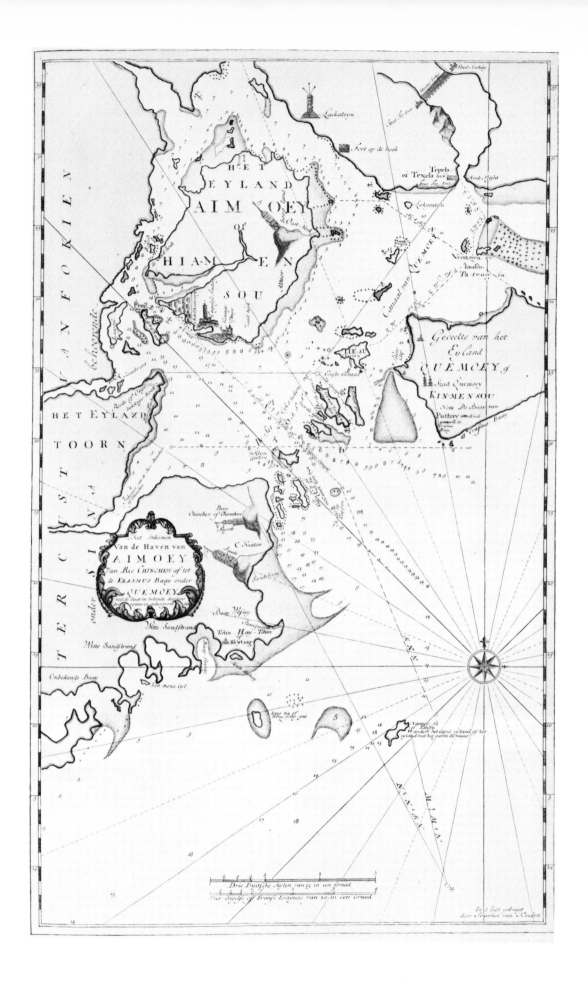

# XXXV

# The Approaches to the Port of Amoy, Fukien

**Johannes Van Keulen,** *the Younger*

*1753*

I : 250,000

HET INKOMEN VAN DE HAVEN VAN AIMONY VAN RIO CHINCHEW AF TOT DE ERASMUS BAAY ONDER QUEMOEY . . . *Signed Johannes Van Keulen. Undated. Coloured chart, engraved on paper, size 280 × 490 mm. Single cartouche, in Dutch. From Johannes Van Keulen II and Jan de Marre's sea atlas* DE NIEUWE GROOTE LICHTENDE ZEE-FAKKEL . . . *Amsterdam, Johannes Van Keulen II, 1753. Dutch black-letter text; engraved and printed titles; 76 pp. Folio. 72 coloured charts.*

---

This chart comes from the celebrated sixth part of the Van Keulens' *Zee-Fakkel* series. It is in effect a detailed and comprehensive pilot-guide to the East Indies, at a time when Dutch discovery and commercial influence in those waters were at their height. After 1743 Johannes Van Keulen II was the sole supplier of charts to the Dutch East India Company and it was by order of the Company and in association with his colleague Jan de Marre, an examiner in navigation for that company who wrote the text, that the atlas was published in 1753. The work is remarkable for its detailed information of East Indian waters.

The chart depicting the approaches to Amoy is particularly interesting for two reasons. Cartographically, note the detailed soundings and sandbanks in the approach channels; the attractive pictorial representation of landmarks, especially pagodas; and the stone bridge NE of Amoy and what appears to be a signal station at Lackateyn nearby. Historically, too, there is interest, for Amoy was the first port through which the Dutch traded with China. Moreover, in the eighteenth century it monopolised the Chinese junk trade southward to the Straits of Malacca and Java—key areas in the Dutch colonial empire.

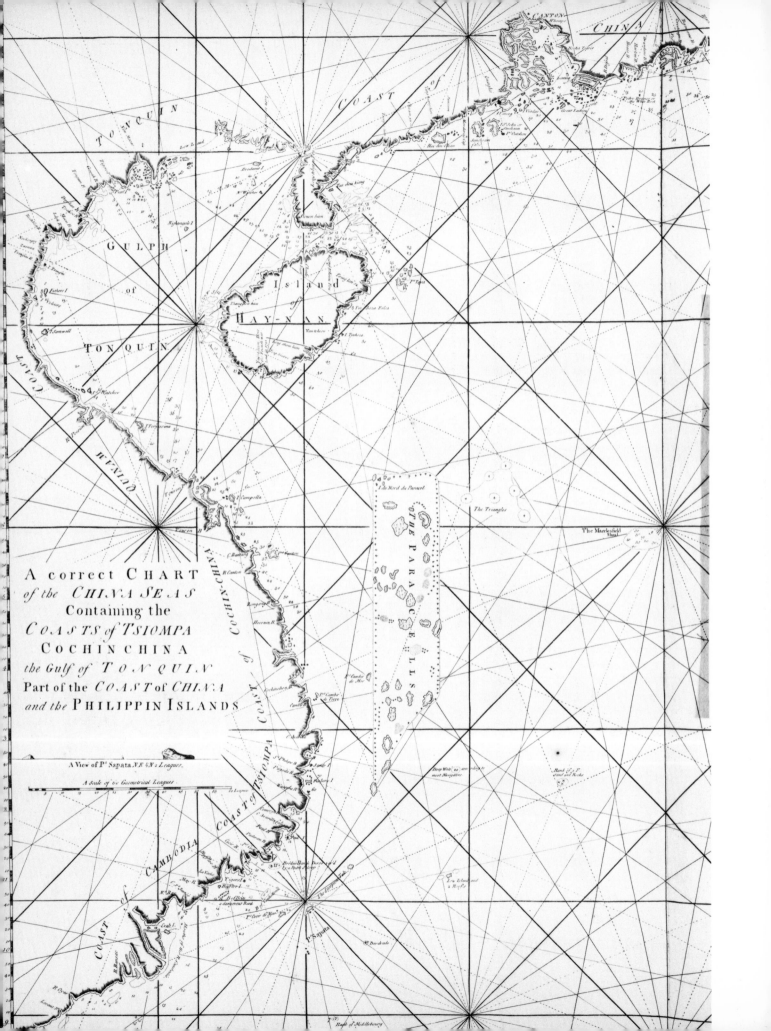

A correct CHART
of the CHINA SEAS
Containing the
COASTS of TSIOMPA
COCHINCHINA
the Gulf of TONQUIN
Part of the COAST of CHINA
and the PHILIPPIN ISLANDS

A View of P.º Sapata NE ½ N 2 Leagues.

A Scale of 60 Geometrical Leagues.

# XXXVI

# The South China Sea

**William Herbert**

*c 1758*

1 : 2,900,000

*Western half of* A CORRECT CHART OF THE CHINA SEAS CONTAINING THE COASTS OF TSIOMPA COCHIN CHINA THE GULF OF TONQUIN PART OF THE COAST OF CHINA . . . *Without signature or date. Plain chart, engraved on paper, 600 × 770 mm. Plane projection. Single cartouche; [bar-scale 'of 60 geometrical leagues']. From William Herbert's sea atlas* A NEW DIRECTORY FOR THE EAST INDIES . . . *London, William Herbert, 1758. Printed title, in black and red; no text. Large folio. 29 charts.*

---

This chart of the passage through the South China Sea, from the latitude of Saigon through to Canton, was prepared when the Honourable East India Company was at the height of its prosperity.

WILLIAM HERBERT (1718–95) is one of the lesser known English cartographers of the eighteenth century. About 1748 he went out to India as a purser's clerk aboard an East Indiaman, whence grew his cartographic interest in the East Indies. In the early 1750s he set up in business on London Bridge as a seller of engravings, prints, and charts.

His main work *A New Directory for the East Indies* . . . was first published in 1758 and proved so popular that a second edition appeared the same year with a number of additional charts. Later editions followed (1767, 1776, etc), some under the editorship of another cartographer, Samuel Dunn. In preparing the *Directory*, Herbert relied heavily on the practical sea knowledge of the scientist and navigator William Nicholson. Herbert also found much material for the charts from the major contemporary French work in this field—D'Après de Mannevillette's *La Neptune Oriental* . . . first published in 1745—which he acknowledges on the title page of his atlas. Note the stylised manner in which the Paracel Islands and the Amphitrite Group (The Triangles) are shown.

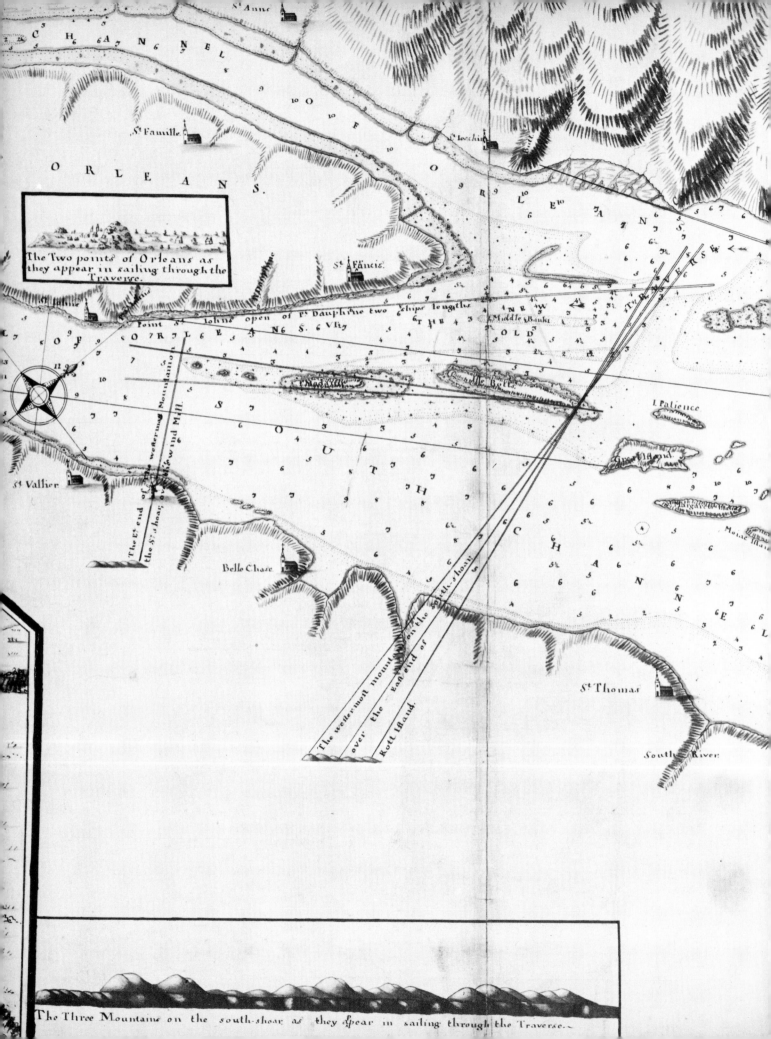

St Anne

ST FAMILLE

ORLEANS.

St Joachim

CHANNEL

The Two points of Orleans as they appear in sailing through the Traverse.

St Fancie

ORLEANS

Point St Johns open of Ft Dauphine two ships lengths

OF ORLEANS

Middle Bank

THE

OLD

THE NEW

TRAVERSE

St Vallier

SOUTH

I. Patience

Great Island

The Extend of the westermost Mountain & the St shoar over the wind Mill

Belle Chase

The westermost mountain on the South shoar over the East end of Roll Island.

CHANNEL

St Thomas

South River

The Three Mountains on the south-shoar as they appear in sailing through the Traverse.

# XXXVII

# St Lawrence River— the Traverse

## James Cook

*[1762]*

1 : 73,000

*Detail from chart signed* TO THE RIGHT HON<sup>BLE</sup> THE LORD COLVILL
REAR ADMIRAL OF THE WHITE SQUADRON OF HIS MAJESTYS FLEET.
THIS CHART OF THE RIVER—S<sup>T</sup>. LAURENCE FROM GREEN ISLAND TO
CAPE CARROUGE IS MOST HUMBLY DEDICATED BY HIS LORDSHIP'S
MOST HUMBLE SERVANT JAM<sup>S</sup> COOK [*with inset:*] A PLAN OF THE
BASON OF QUEBEC. MS *chart on paper, handcoloured, 510 × 3,040
mm. Plane projection.*

General Wolfe's successful assault on Quebec in 1759 during
the Seven Years' War was only possible because ships of the
British Navy were able to navigate the tortuous channels of the
St Lawrence River, despite the fact that the French had removed all aids to navigation. One of those who took part in this
enterprise was James Cook, (1729–79), then master of HMS
*Pembroke*, sixty guns, and later to become the famous
navigator.

The illustration opposite—a very small part of a 10-ft long
manuscript 'fair chart' drawn by Cook himself some years after
the assault—shows the most difficult part of the passage up the
river—the Traverse, just east of the Ile d'Orléans, and some
30 miles downstream from Quebec itself, where the main ship-
channel changes from the north to the south bank.

On 8 June 1759 boats of the British fleet, with Cook on
board, started to sound the Traverse, and on 14 June ships of
the Fleet passed up the Traverse. The French, who had looked
upon the navigational hazards of the St Lawrence as one of their
most efficient defences, were amazed. The French commander,
Montcalm, in a letter written on 25 June, noted acidly, 'our
best seamen or pilots seem to me to be either liars or ignor-
amuses'.

The city was captured on 13 September 1759. On 23 September Cook became master of the *Northumberland*, seventy guns,
wearing the broad pendant of Commodore Lord Colvill.

During the next two years the *Northumberland* spent the
winters in ice-free Halifax, Nova Scotia, returning to the St
Lawrence for the summers of 1760 and 1761, when Cook
carried out more surveys. Having spent the summer of 1762 in
Newfoundland waters, Colvill took the *Northumberland* home,
reaching Spithead on 25 October 1762. Colvill was immediately
promoted to Rear Admiral of the White, and returned to North
America in the *Romney*.

There are three copies, all undated, of Cook's 'fair sheets',
giving the results of his surveys of the St Lawrence of 1759–61:

(a) an unsigned copy lacking topography, in the Hydrographic
Department;
(b) a signed copy, once the property of Admiral Sir W. Fanshawe Martin (1801–95), now in the Public Archives of
Canada;
(c) a signed copy, part of which is reproduced opposite, lent to
the National Maritime Museum by the British Admiralty in
1946, which seems to be the latest of the three—as it is dedicated to Colvill as a Rear Admiral, it was presumably drawn
after October 1762, but probably before Cook sailed for
Newfoundland once more in May 1763.

Contrary to the suggestions of some writers, Thomas Jeffery's
*A New Chart of the River St. Lawrence* of 1760 (published in
Sayer & Bennett's *North-American Pilot* of 1775) could not have
been derived from these MS charts of Cook's, which were
definitely drawn later. Cook did, however, contribute to
Jeffery's 1760 chart.

In December 1762 Colvill wrote to the Admiralty about the
draughts and observations that Cook had laid before their
Lordships, finishing his letter: '. . . I think him well fitted for
the work he has undertaken, and for greater undertakings of the
same kind'. And so it was to prove, as we shall see in Chart
XLII.

## Bibliography

Hydrographic Department Professional Paper No 13 (1950)
'Selected Manuscript Documents of Historic Importance
Preserved in the Archives of the Department'

Stacey, C. P. *Quebec 1759* (Toronto, 1959), 42

Skelton, R. A. 'Captain James Cook as a Hydrographer',
*The Mariners' Mirror*, Vol 40, No 2 (1954), 99

Tooley, R. V. and Skelton, R. A. 'The Marine Survey of James
Cook in North America, 1758–1768', *Map Collectors' Circle*,
no 37 (1967), 13–14

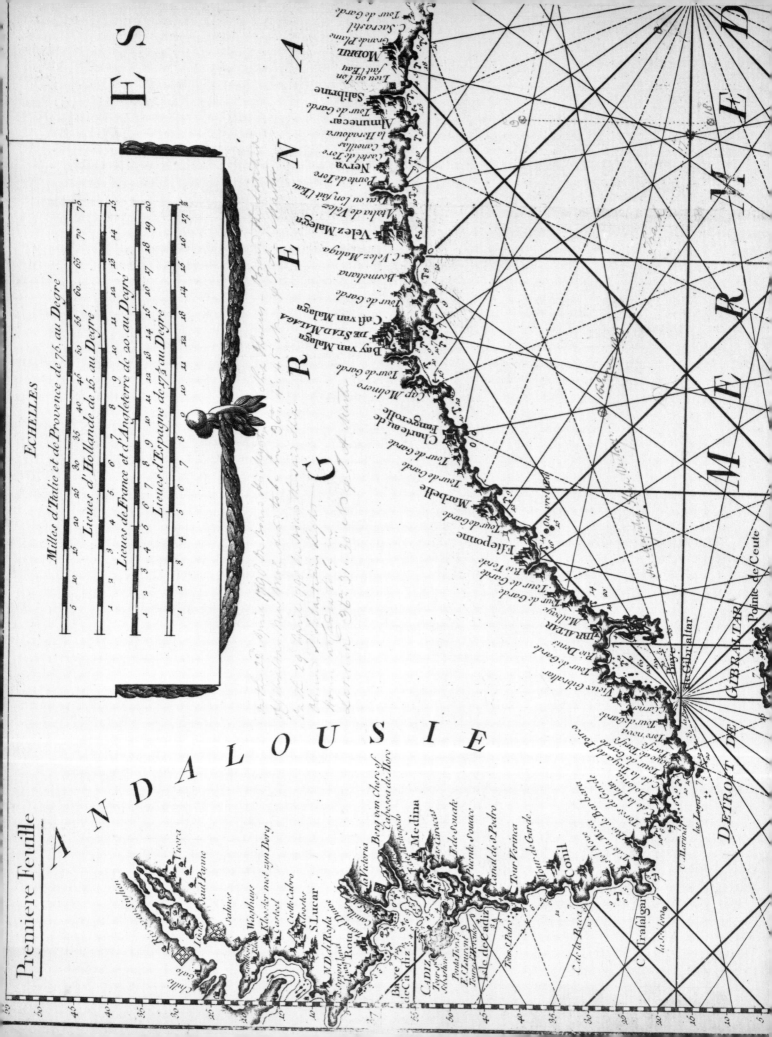

# XXXVIII

# Western Mediterranean and the Strait of Gibraltar

## Joseph Roux with MS additions

### 1764

### 1 : 685,000

*Detail from* CARTE DE LA MER MEDITERRANÉE EN DOUZE FEUILLES. DEDIEE A M^gr LE DUC DE CHOISEUL . . . MINISTRE DE LA GUERRE ET DE LA MARINE PAR SON TRÈS HUMBLE SERVITEUR JOSEPH ROUX HYDROGRAPHE DU ROY, SUR LE PORT À ST. JEAN, À MARSEILLE. . . . PREMIÈRE FEUILLE. *Signed Joseph Roux. Dated 1764. Engraved on paper, with important manuscript plotting of ships' tracks and notes added. Single cartouche. 550 × 790 mm. Plane projection. From Joseph Roux's bound set of twelve sea charts of the Mediterranean* CARTE DE LA MER MEDITERRANÉE EN DOUZE FEUILLES . . ., *being the first chart of the set. Marseilles, Roux, 1764. No title or text. Folio. 12 charts.*

---

The interest of this particular copy of one of Roux's Mediterranean charts is historic rather than cartographic, since it was used in HMS *Victory*, Lord Nelson's flagship, in 1803 and 1805. The atlas in which it is contained belonged to Thomas Atkinson, the master, and on the various charts therein he has marked the *Victory*'s tracks and fixes, first between 16 June and 29 July 1803, when she sailed from Gibraltar to Valletta and then to join Lord Nelson off Toulon; second between 22 January and 16 February 1805, when Nelson, hearing that the French fleet had left Toulon, sailed with the British Fleet from Sardinia in darkness, passed through the Straits of Messina in formation (an unparalleled feat under sail), and swept as far east as Alexandria before returning to Sardinia. There are also manuscript observations indicating that the chart was used earlier on board HMS *Theseus*, in April 1798.

This atlas also highlights another fact. Ships of the Royal Navy had to rely on privately published charts, British and foreign until 1795, when Alexander Dalrymple was appointed to set up what amounted to a state hydrographic service. But here, ten years later, the flagship of the British Fleet was still using forty-year-old French charts.

Little is known about Joseph Roux, a hydrographer by royal appointment, who ran a chart-publishing business in Marseilles. As a companion work to his charts of the Méditerranean he published, also in 1764, an atlas depicting 121 ports and anchorages in the Mediterranean called *Recueil des principaux plans des ports et rades de la Mer Mediterranee* . . . It was a popular work, later editions following in 1779 and 1817.

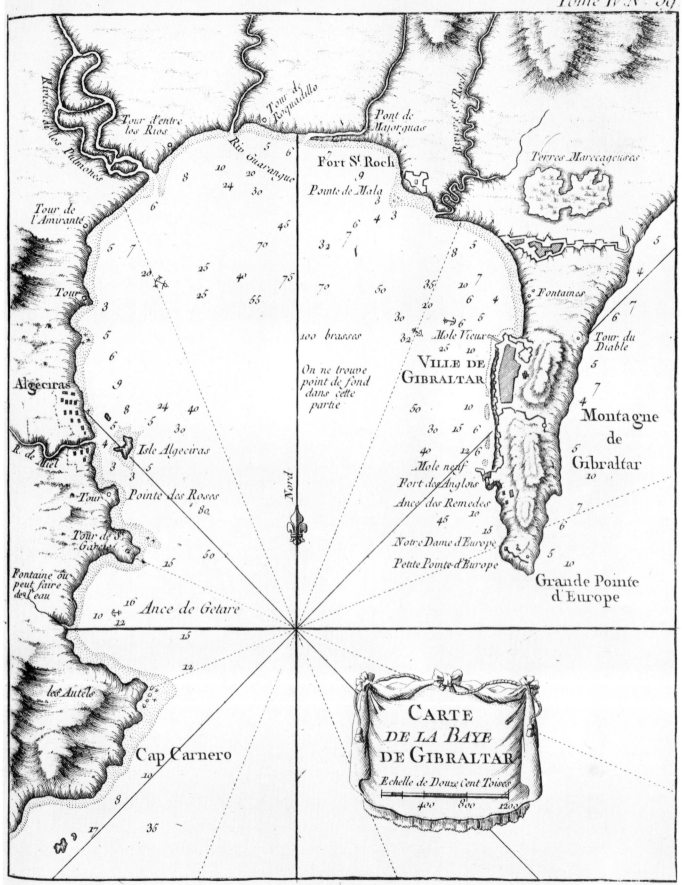

Rivière de los Palmones

Tour d'entre los Rios

Tour de Roquadillo

Pont de Majorguas

Rio Guarangue

Terres Marecageuses

Fort St. Roch
9
Pointe de Mala
3

Tour de l'Amirauté

Tour

Algeciras

Isle Algeciras

R. de Miel

Tour

Pointe des Roses

Tour de St. Garcia

Fontaine ou peut faire de l'eau

100 brasses

On ne trouve point de fond dans cette partie

VILLE DE GIBRALTAR

Fontaines

Tour du Diable

Mole Vieux

Montagne de Gibraltar

Mole neuf

Fort des Anglois

Ance des Remedes

Notre Dame d'Europe

Petite Pointe d'Europe

Grande Pointe d'Europe

Nord

Ance de Getare

les Autels

Cap Carnero

CARTE DE LA BAYE DE GIBRALTAR

Echelle de Douze Cent Toises

400    800    1200

# XXXIX

**Bibliography**

Anon. 'Notice sur le Service Hydrographique de la Marine', *Annales hydrographiques* (Paris, 1914), 9–10

# *Gibraltar Bay*
## Jacques Nicolas Bellin
## *1764*
## 1 : 60,000

CARTE DE LA BAYE DE GIBRALTAR. *Unsigned; undated. Plain chart, engraved on paper, size 175 × 220 mm. Single cartouche, with bar-scale,* Echelle de Douze Cent Toises, *therein. From Bellin's atlas* LE PETIT ATLAS MARITIME . . . *Paris, Bellin, 1764. Five volumes. No text; engraved titles and table of contents to each volume. Small Folio. 580 charts. Volume IV (128 charts): . . .* contenant L'Europe et les divers Etats qu'elle renferme excepté la France, *chart no 59.*

---

In contrast to the British Navy, France had set up a State hydrographic service—*Le Dépôt des Cartes et Plans de la Marine*—in 1720. Jacques Nicolas Bellin (1703–72) joined the new office at the age of eighteen in 1721, being the first *Ingénieur hydrographe de la Marine*, a post he held until his death in 1772.

During his term of office, he prepared a large number of charts, most of which he signed *Sieur Bellin*. His most important atlases were:

*Le Neptune François*, with charts of the Atlantic coasts of Europe, a revision of the *Neptune* of 1693 (see Chart XXXII), first published in 1753;

*L'Hydrographie Françoise*, with charts of the rest of the world, first published in 1756;

*Le Petit Atlas Maritime*, with 580 charts of the whole world in five volumes, in smaller format.

The chart opposite occurs in volume IV of the last atlas, whose contents are arranged geographically—volume I, North America and the Caribbean; II, South America; III, Africa and Asia; IV, Europe, apart from France; and V, the coasts of France. Many of the charts in *Le Petit Atlas Maritime* are reproductions in reduced size of charts prepared for Bellin's previous atlases, but there is also a large amount of fresh material.

The chart of Gibraltar Bay is typical of Bellin's work in the smaller format. A point of interest is the use of curved hachuring in the engraving to emphasise the coastline and river courses. Note how this is contrasted with the representation of hill slopes, where straight hachure lines are used.

Soundings are in *brasses* (already mentioned) of 5 French feet, or slightly less than 5ft 4in in English measurement. Distances are in *toises*, each a fraction less than 6ft 4in in English measurement.

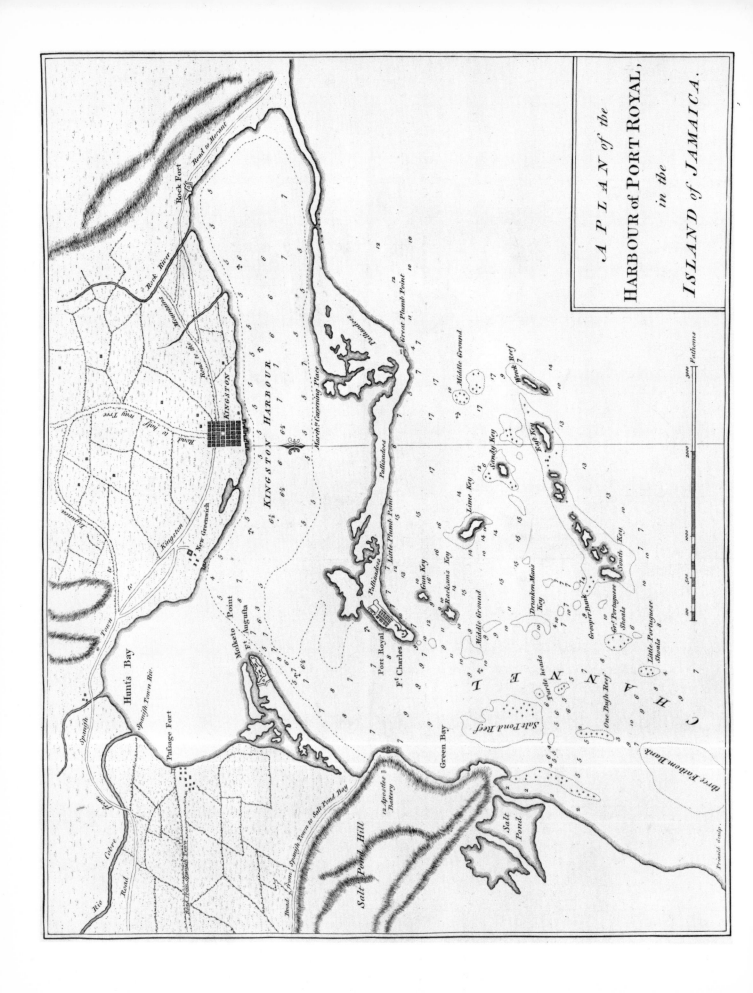

# XL

# The Harbour of Port Royal, Jamaica

**Captain** Joseph Speer

*c 1766*

## 1 : 58,000

A PLAN OF THE HARBOUR OF PORT ROYAL, IN THE ISLAND OF JAMAICA. *No signature or date; engraver's imprint,* Prinald Sculp., *bottom left of chart. Plain chart, engraved on paper, 270 × 355 mm. Plane projection. Single cartouche. From Speer's* THE WEST-INDIA PILOT . . . *London, 1766. Printed title; ii, 53 pp. Folio. 13 charts.*

---

Very little is known about Captain Speer, but his *West India Pilot* epitomises the great English interest in the Caribbean throughout the eighteenth century, principally as a result of the rapid growth of the sugar trade. The chart reproduced here is accurate and clear, and is accompanied by well written sailing directions.

Those who know Jamaica will be able to recognise many of the features, except, perhaps, in the central area of Kingston. Today the docks area is NW of the old part of Kingston seen here, Hunt's Bay is being reclaimed, and the airport covers the Pallisadoes and the Careening Place.

The chart comes from the first edition of the atlas. A second edition appeared in 1774, with the number of charts increased to twenty-six, and there was also a third, published after 1776, in which two further charts were added.

This copy of the atlas contains a manuscript entry by the author at the end of the dedication (p ii) which reads: 'Examined and corrected by me Joseph Smith Speer'.

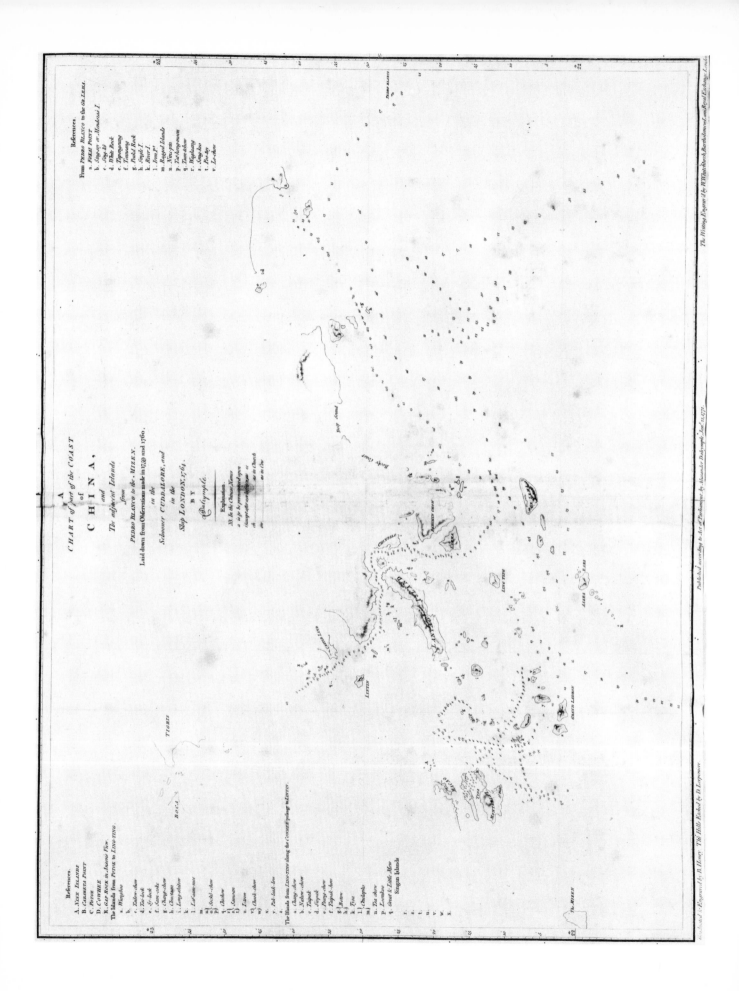

A
CHART of part of the COAST
of
C H I N A,
and
The adjacent Islands
from
PEDRO BLANCO to the ~ MIZEN.
Laid down from Observations made in 1759 and 1760.
in the
Schooner CUDDALORE, and
in the
Ship LONDON, 1764.
BY
Dalrymple.

Explanation

References.
From PEDRO BLANCO to the GR.LEMA.
a. FORAI POINT
b. Sing-ay or~Mendozal I.
c. Sing-kil
d. White Rock
e. Tignoguang
f. Tamaong
g. Packol Rock
h. Single I.
k. River I.
l. Forn Pt
m. Ragged Islands
n. New-pin
p. Tie-hongmoon
q. Tam-tchow
r. Wagkang
s. Song-koo
t. Poo-toy
v. Le-chow

References.
A. NEW ISLANDS
B. CHACHEU POINT
C. PUTOU
D. COFFRE
R. OAR ROCK nr. Aiaou Few.
The Islands from PUTOU to LINE-TING.
a. Plangkou
b.
c. Tation-chow
d. Tie-kok
e. Sy-kok
f. Sam-cako
g. Chang-chow
h. Chootam
i. Long-chiktow
l. Lat-sam-mee
m. Sookë-chow
o.
o. Chutow
t. Aimoon
u. Lixou
w. Chuck-chow
x.
v. Pak-lack-low
The Islands from LINE-TING along the COAST passing to LIXOU.
a. Chang-chow
b. Nathow-chow
d. Taipak
e. Kaypak
f. Duay-chow
g. Taipak-ham
h. Notow
i. Fou
l. Buckpko
m. Tsi-chow
n. Lonebow
p. Goat & Litt. Mew
q. Singan Islands
r.
s.
t.
u.
w.
x.

TIGRIS

BOCA

Ty. MIZEN

# XLI

# Approaches to Canton

**Alexander Dalrymple**

*1771*

$1 : 375,000$

A CHART OF PART OF THE COAST OF CHINA, AND THE ADJACENT ISLANDS FROM PEDRO BLANCO TO THE MIZEN. LAID DOWN FROM OBSERVATIONS MADE IN 1759 AND 1760 IN THE SCHOONER CUDDA-LORE, AND IN THE SHIP LONDON, 1764. BY A. DALRYMPLE . . . PUBLISHED ACCORDING TO ACT OF PARLIAMENT BY ALEXANDER DALRYMPLE, JAN^y. 21, 1771. *Signed and dated. Plane chart, engraved on paper, 465 × 610 mm. Single cartouche: reference keys on left- and right-hand side of chart; imprint and names of engravers at foot. From a bound collection of charts and plans by Alexander Dalrymple and others. London, Dalrymple, c [1792]. No title or text. Folio. 34 charts and plans.*

---

When this chart was published, the only port open to European trade on the mainland of China was Canton, the approaches to which can be seen here. In the SW corner is the island of *Macao*, a Portuguese colony since 1557. Here, the anchorage of the *Tipa* (or *Typa*) was used by East Indiamen of all western nations as a convoy assembly port, but very considerable shoaling has taken place since then. *Boca Tigris* (the tiger's mouth) to the NW is at the mouth of the Canton River, whence East Indiamen sailed up to the anchorage of Whampoa, a few miles below Canton itself, where the European traders had their 'factories'.

The city of Hong Kong did not then exist, its port not being developed until after 1842, when the island here called *Fanchin Chow* (centre, now called Victoria Island) was ceded to Britain. The main (eastern) channel into Hong Kong harbour—the Tathong Channel—lies between the island marked *p*—*Tat-hong-moon*—and the islands marked *q*, *r*, and *s*; the western, or West Lamma Channel passes to the west and north of *Lamma*, *Fanchin Chow* and today's Green Island, here marked *f*.

ALEXANDER DALRYMPLE (1737–1808) was appointed Hydrographer to the East India Company in 1779 and then in 1795 the Admiralty made him Hydrographer to the Navy (see Chart LI) —a post he kept until shortly before his death in 1808. For many years Dalrymple was obsessed with the idea of the existence of a large southern Continent, even after Cook's discoveries to the contrary during his second voyage. Partly to support his theories, Dalrymple spent many years collecting hundreds of charts of the East Indies, Far East, and the southern oceans, and made great efforts to correlate the hydrographic discoveries of earlier navigators and, in his charts, link them with more recent discoveries.

In 1774 he published *A Collection of plans of ports, etc. in the East Indies, with some nautical instructions and explanations . . .*, initially with nineteen charts and plans. The chart of the China coast illustrated here, however, is derived from a much larger collection of charts and plans bound up as an atlas and issued without title or text.

**Bibliography**

Fry, Howard T. *Alexander Dalrymple and the expansion of British Trade* (1970)

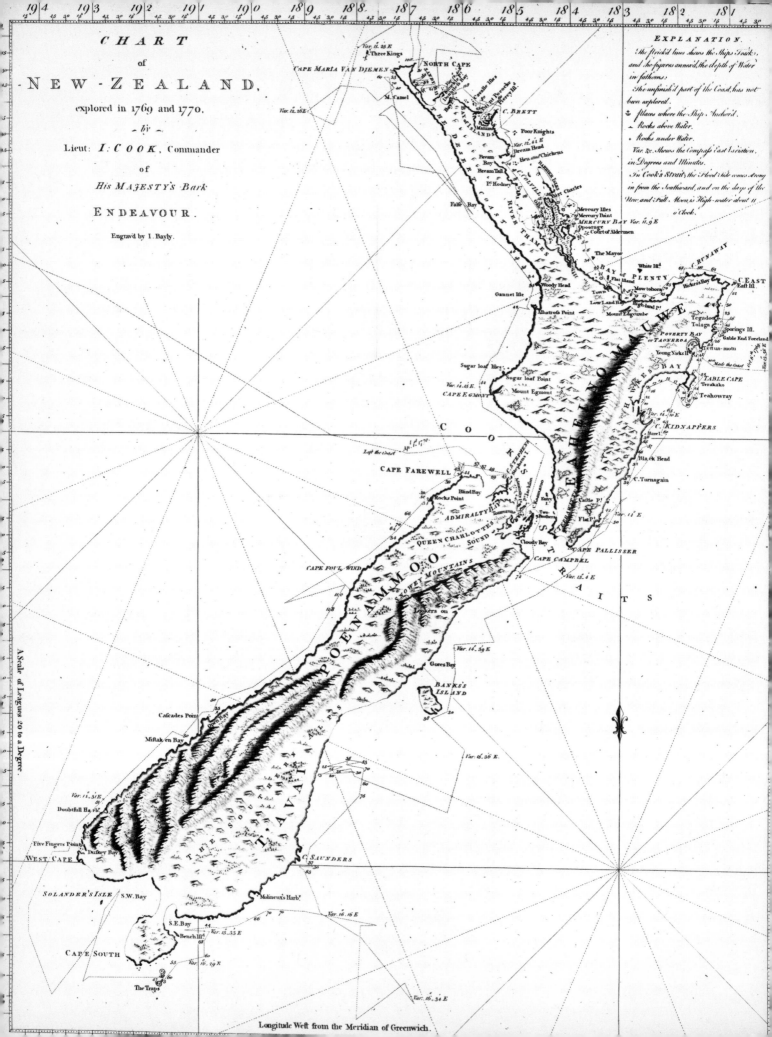

CHART
of
NEW-ZEALAND,
explored in 1769 and 1770.
by
Lieut: I. COOK, Commander
of
His MAJESTY'S Bark
ENDEAVOUR.

Engravd by I. Bayly.

EXPLANATION.

The strickd lines shews the Ships Track,
and the figures annex'd, the depth of Water
in fathoms.
The unfinish'd part of the Coast, has not
been explored.
⚓ Places where the Ship Anchor'd.
Rocks above Water.
Rocks under Water.
Var. &c. Shews the Compass East Variation,
in Degrees and Minutes.
In Cook's Strait, the Flood Tide comes strong
in from the Southward, and on the days of the
New and Full Moon, is High-water about 11
o'Clock.

A Scale of Leagues 20 to a Degree.

Longitude West from the Meridian of Greenwich.

# XLII

# New Zealand

## James Cook

### 1772

### 1 : 3,650,000 (40° s)

CHART OF NEW ZEALAND EXPLORED IN 1769 AND 1770 BY LIEUT. I. COOK, COMMANDER OF HIS MAJESTY'S BARK ENDEAVOUR. ENGRAVED BY I. BAYLY. PUBLISH'D AS THE ACT DIRECTS 1ST. JAN.Y. 1772. *Engraved chart on paper, 495 × 382 mm. Mercator's projection. From J. Hawkesworth's* AN ACCOUNT OF THE VOYAGES UNDERTAKEN BY THE ORDER OF HIS PRESENT MAJESTY FOR MAKING DISCOVERIES IN THE SOUTHERN HEMISPHERE, *II (1773).*

---

The overt purpose of James Cook's first Pacific voyage from 1768 to 1771 was to go to Tahiti and observe the transit of Venus across the disk of the sun on 3 June 1769. Cook thus took part in the first organised international scientific venture. But his voyage also had a strategic purpose, which was revealed when, after the transit, he opened a sealed packet containing secret additional instructions. First, he was to search the South Pacific between 35° and 40° s for any sign of a Great Southern Continent. By this date few believed in the existence of such a continent, but, if it did exist, England wanted to discover it before France. He was then to sail westward 'until you discover it [the continent], or fall in with the Eastern side of the Land, discovered by Tasman and now called New Zealand . . . But if you should fail of discovering the Continent before-mentioned, you will upon falling in with New Zealand carefully observe the Latitude and Longitude in which that Land is situated, and explore as much of the Coast as the Condition of the Bark [the Endeavour], the health of her crew, and the State of youre Provisions will admit of . . .'

Cook did not discover the Continent, but he carried out his other instructions. In something under six months, between October 1769 and March 1770, he circumnavigated both islands of New Zealand, sailing nearly 5,000 nautical miles and carrying out the brilliant running survey that resulted in the chart opposite. Geographically, his discoveries can best be summarised in his own words: 'This country, which before now was thought to be part of the imaginary southern continent, consists of Two large Islands divided from each other by a strait or passage of 4 or 6 Leagues broad . . .'

On the chart the shape of the two islands is very close to reality, and almost all the placenames are those in use today. Latitudes are excellent, as would be expected, but longitudes are not all as accurate as they could have been. Except near Mercury Bay in North Island (where the position was determined by lunar distances taken afloat off the entrance to the Bay) and on the SE coast of South Island, the whole country is placed too far to the east, mostly by about 25'. Surprisingly, one of the larger errors (40') occurred at Queen Charlotte's Sound, where the ship stayed three weeks.

Geographical positions were obtained astronomically, a few by Cook himself but most by Charles Green (1735-71), a professional astronomer sent by the Royal Society to observe the transit. The sophisticated instruments used ashore at Tahiti were available but were not landed in New Zealand, and all observations were made with Hadley sextants or quadrants, mostly while the ship was under way, though sometimes at anchor.

On this, his first Pacific voyage, Cook did not carry a marine timekeeper, so that all longitudes had to be found by the method of lunar distances. He was, however, the first explorer to have the benefit of the *Nautical Almanac*, first published for the year 1767, which halved the time taken to work out a 'lunar'; though it only ran up to the end of 1769, the ephemerides for 1770 and 1771 not being completed before he left England.

## Bibliography

Beaglehole, J. C. *The Journals of Captain James Cook: I—The Voyage of the Endeavour 1768-1771* (Cambridge, 1968), cclxxxii-iii; also 284

Maling, P. B. *Early Charts of New Zealand, 1542–1851* (Wellington, etc, 1969), 36–54 but particularly 44

Skelton, R. A. 'Captain James Cook as a Hydrographer', *The Mariners' Mirror*, Vol 40, No 2 (1954), 109–13, which gives an excellent map illustrating Cook's errors

Wales, William. *Astronomical Observations made in the Voyages which were undertaken by order of His Present Majesty for making Discoveries in the Southern Hemisphere . . .* (1788), 108–27

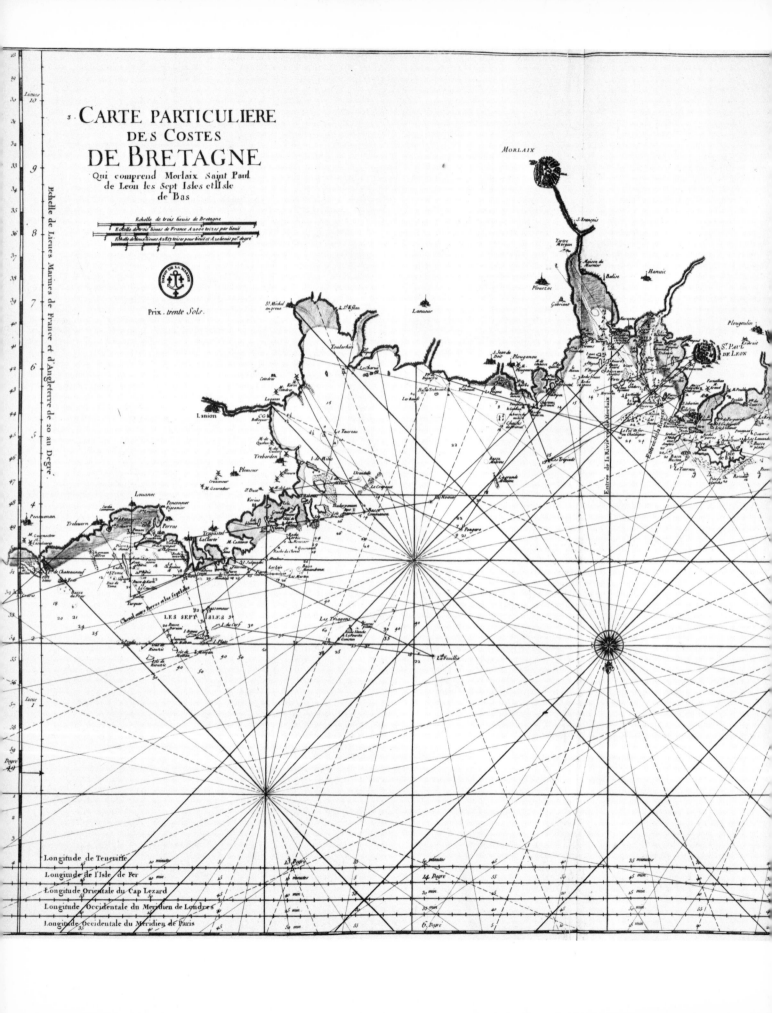

# CARTE PARTICULIERE
## DES COSTES
# DE BRETAGNE
Qui comprend Morlaix Saint Paul
de Leon les Sept Isles et l'Isle
de Bas

Echelle de trois lieues de Bretagne

Echelle de trois lieues de France A 2000 toises par lieuë

Echelle de deux lieues A 2857 toises pour lieuë A 20 lieuës p.r degre

Prix. trente Sols.

MORLAIX

Plougoulin

S.t PAVL
DE LEON

Louanec

LES SEPT ISLES

Longitude de Teneriffe

Longitude de l'Isle de Fer

Longitude Orientale du Cap Lezard

Longitude Occidentale du Meridien de Londres

Longitude Occidentale du Meridien de Paris

# XLIII

# Part of the Coast of Brittany, including Morlaix and Les Sept Isles

**Jacques Nicolas Bellin** *et alia*

*[c 1773, from the original of 1693]*

1 : 127,000

*Detail from* CARTE PARTICULIÈRE DES COSTES DE BRETAGNE QUI COMPREND MORLAIX SAINT PAUL DE LEON LES SEPT ISLES ET L'ISLE DE BAS . . . DÉPÔT DE LA MARINE . . . PRIX. TRENTE SOLS. [*Special chart of the Brittany coast, including Morlaix, St Paul de Leon, the Seven Islands and Low Island . . .*]. *Unsigned; undated. Plane chart, engraved on paper, 590 × 810 mm. North at the bottom. Single cartouche, with bar-scale and official 'Dépôt de la Marine' stamp underneath. From Bellin's sea atlas* LE NEPTUNE FRANÇOIS . . . *Versailles, L'Imprimerie du Département de la Marine, 1773–93]. French text; engraved & printed titles; [8] pp, Large Folio. 66 charts.*

---

Though *Le Neptune François* of 1693 was prepared under official auspices (see Chart XXXII), the actual publication seems to have been done privately, the plates remaining the property of the publishers and their successors. By the 1740s, some of the plates had been dispersed or lost and complete copies of the atlas became very rare, fetching high prices in both France and Holland.

In 1751, the surviving plates were acquired by the Navy and the Minister Rouille gave orders that a new edition of the *Neptune* was to be published, this time officially. The *Dépôt des Cartes et Plans de la Marine* engraved two new plates to replace those that were lost, and added longitude graduations (or amended those that were wrong) on to the surviving plates. A general chart of Brittany which had been engraved in 1693 but never published, was added, and the revised atlas published in 1753. An additional preface by the editor, J. N. Bellin, gave the history of the atlas and detailed the sources of individual charts.

The *Neptune François* and its companion *L'Hydrographie Françoise* were reissued at intervals in the eighteenth century until, from 1800, they were replaced by the elaborate and magnificent *Le Neptune Français* which covered the whole world in eleven volumes. The individual volumes gathered the charts geographically: for instance, I, *Neptune des côtes septentrionales d'Europe* (thirty-six charts); and IX, *Neptune de l'Amérique meridionale* (forty charts). While incorporating revised material and recent hydrographic discoveries, the series owed a great deal to the work of earlier pioneers in French hydrography—notably Bellin himself, Jaillot, D'Après de Mannevillette, and Beautemps-Beaupré.

The chart reproduced here, from a late-eighteenth-century *Neptune*, is printed from the 1693 plate, based on de la Voye's surveys of 1675, to which has been added (a) Bellin's latitude and longitude graduation in 1753, and (b) the Dépôt's stamp and the price of 30 sols in about 1770.

Two features typical of French charts of this period are the multiple longitude scales and the multiple scales of distance—symptomatic of the confusion that prevailed before the days of international standardisation. Until the International Meridian Conference of 1884 chose Greenwich as the world's prime meridian, each country pleased itself in this respect, often choosing as zero the meridian of its state observatory. The longitude scales on this chart are based on the Isle de Fer, or Hierro, the westernmost of the Canary Islands (Fortunate Islands), in early times accounted the most westerly of known lands and chosen by Ptolemy as his prime meridian; Tenerife in the Canary Islands; the Lizard in Cornwall, often the point of departure for ocean voyages; London (St Paul's Cathedral), for Greenwich came to be used by the British only after the *Nautical Almanac* commenced publication in 1767; and Paris, the observatory.

The bar-scales show Breton leagues, French leagues at 2,000 toises per league (see Chart XXXIX), and English leagues (here just called leagues) at 2,853 toises per league and 20 leagues per degree.

This chart of Brittany, first published in 1693, appeared in successive editions of the *Neptune* until 1824. The price of the chart reproduced here was 30 sols, but rose to 40 sols soon after the Revolution in 1789, and had become 1½ francs by 1824.

Immediately after the Revolution the fleur-de-lis on the compass roses on many charts in the *Neptune* (see Fig 1) were replaced by a cap of liberty (Fig 2). In the 1824 edition some charts reverted to the fleur-de-lis while others adopted the representation of the compass needle.

### Bibliography

Bellin, J. N. 'Remarques sur les cartes du Neptune François dont les Planches ont été remises au Dépôt des Plans de la Marine en 1753', *Le Neptune François . . . Premier Volume* (Paris, 1753), Preface

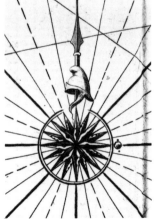

*Fig XLIII-1.* Compass rose with fleur-de-lis at north point, as used before the Revolution

*Fig XLIII-2.* With Cap of Liberty, as used immediately after the Revolution

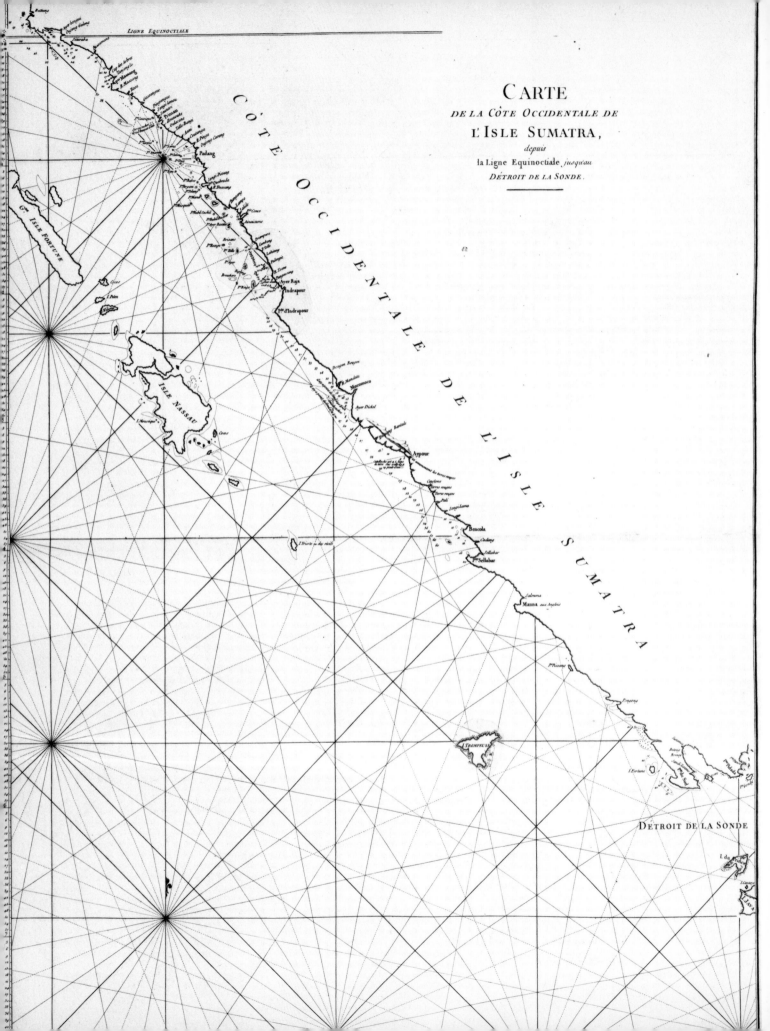

CARTE
DE LA CÔTE OCCIDENTALE DE
L'ISLE SUMATRA,
depuis
la Ligne Equinoctiale jusqu'au
DÉTROIT DE LA SONDE.

LIGNE EQUINOCTIALE

CÔTE OCCIDENTALE DE L'ISLE SUMATRA

G.ᵉ ISLE FORTUNE

ISLE NASSAU

Padang

Ayer Raja
Indrapour
P.ᵗᵉ d'Indrapour

Moucomoco

Ayer-Dickel

Aypour

Bencola
Cadang
Sellabar
P.ᵗᵉ Sellabar

Salemma
Manna aux Anglois

I. TROMPEUSE

DETROIT DE LA SONDE

# XLIV

# Sumatra—West Coast
## Jean-Baptiste D'Apres de Mannevillette
## *[1775]*
## 1 : 1,440,000

*Western half of* CARTE DE LA CÔTE OCCIDENTALE DE L'ISLE SUMATRA, DEPUIS LA LIGNE EQUINOCTIALE, JUSQU'AU DÉTROIT DE LA SONDE. *Signed by the engraver, Guillaume De La Haye. Undated. Plane chart, engraved on paper, with paste-on corrections in two places. 485 × 660 mm. North to the left. From D'Après de Mannevillette's sea-atlas* LE NEPTUNE ORIENTAL . . . *Paris/ Demonville; Brest/Malassis, 1775. French text. Engraved and printed titles; x; 104 pp. Folio. 63 uncoloured charts.*

---

D'APRÈS DE MANNEVILLETTE (1707–80) was a distinguished navigator, among the first of his countrymen to use Hadley's quadrant, and one of the first hydrographers in France. Late in life he became a personal friend of Dalrymple.

His father was a ship's captain in the service of the French West India Company and in 1726 d'Après visited the Caribbean aboard *Le Maréchal d'Estrées.* From 1735 he began collecting charts and material on the navigation of the African coast and the East Indies, travelling extensively for the purpose. In 1742 he informed the directors of the Compagnie des Indes of his plans for publishing a hydrographic atlas, and, with their approval and the support of L'Académie des Sciences, the work appeared in 1745 as *Le Neptune Oriental.* It was at once hailed as a major achievement and welcomed by navigators throughout the world. In 1762 d'Après was appointed director of an office established by the Compagnie des Indes to publish charts of the East Indies. For thirty years he corrected and improved *Le Neptune Oriental,* with the result that the second augmented edition of 1775—whence this chart comes—comprised sixty-three charts in contrast to the twenty-two of the original work. His final atlas of 1781 was *Le Supplement au Neptune Oriental,* which was based on additional charts and notes discovered among his papers after his death.

The chart of Sumatra illustrated is particularly interesting because it contains two prominent paste-on corrections (see Figs 1 and 2), a method of bringing charts up-to-date still used today.

*Fig XLIV-1*. Paste-on correction

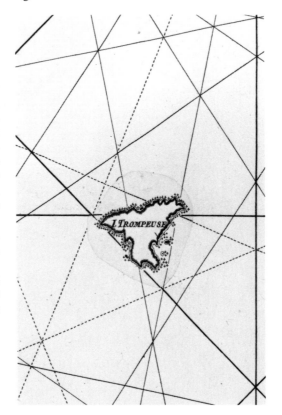

*Fig XLIV-2*. Paste-on correction

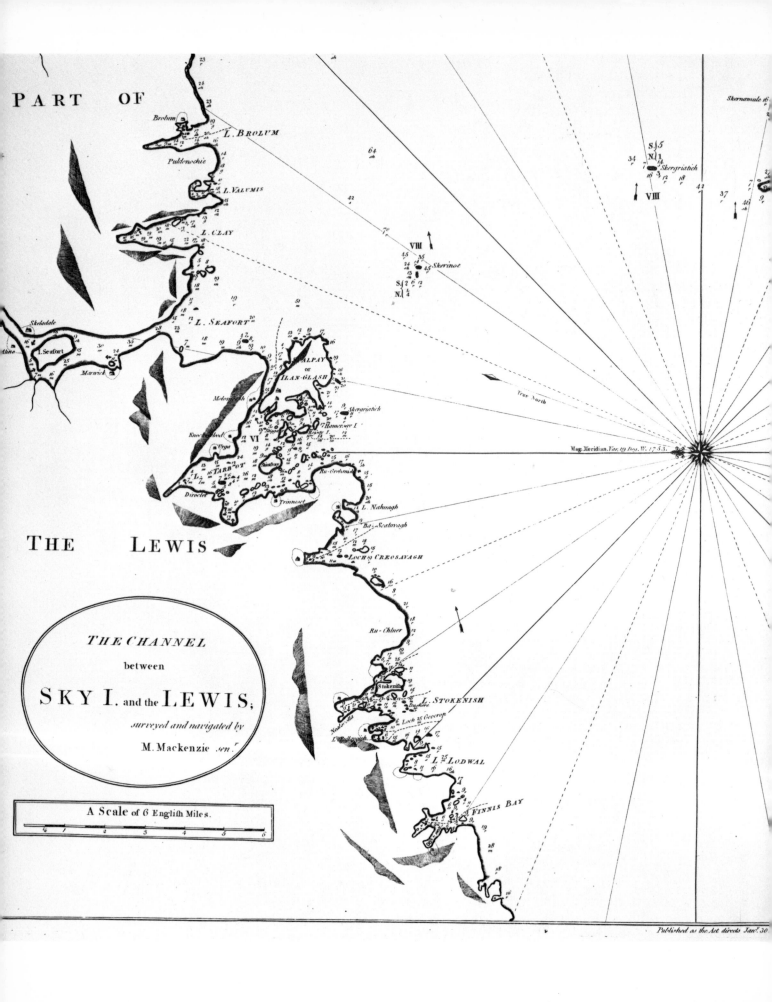

PART OF

THE LEWIS

*Brolum*
L. BROLUM
*Puldonochie*
L. VALVMIS
L. CLAY

L. SEAFORT

*Skelidale*
I. Seafort
*Marwick*

ALPAY
or
ILAN-GLASH

*Skergriatich*
*Hamerow I.*

VI

L. TARBOT
*Directer*
*Trinnaset*

*Ru-Grelsmal*

L. Nahuagh
Ba. Scalavagh
Loch CREOSAVAGH

Ru - Chluer

Stokenill
L. STOKENISH
Loch Geocrop
L. Tullyvagh
L. LODWAL

FINNIS BAY

Skernamule 16

S.J 5
N.J 1
34   Skergriatich
VIII

True North

Mag. Meridian. Var. 19 Deg. W. 1753.

VIII
Skerinoe
S.J
N.J

64

*THE CHANNEL*
between
SKY I. and the LEWIS;
*surveyed and navigated by*
M. Mackenzie *sen.*

A Scale of 6 Englifh Miles.

Published as the Act directs Jan.r 30

# XLV

# Part of the Island of Lewis and the Minches

## Murdoch Mackenzie, *Senior*

### 1776
### 1 : 65,000

*Detail from* THE CHANNEL BETWEEN SKYE AND THE LEWIS; SURVEYED AND NAVIGATED BY M. MACKENZIE SEN[r] . . . PUBLISHED AS THE ACT DIRECTS JAN[y] 30TH 1776. *Signed Murdoch Mackenzie, Senior. Dated 1776. Plane chart, engraved on paper, 665 × 540 mm. Single cartouche. From Murdoch Mackenzie, Senior's atlas* A MARITIM SURVEY OF IRELAND AND THE WEST OF GREAT BRITAIN . . . VOL. II . . . *London, 1776. Title; index of contents. Large Folio. 31 charts.*

---

Murdoch Mackenzie, SENIOR (1712–97), was an Admiralty hydrographer, surveyor, and chart-maker of distinction. His survey of the Orkneys, begun in 1742, was particularly important because the charts were based on a rigid triangulation framework and measured baseline for the first time in British marine cartography. He also used a system of conventional signs and abbreviations (Fig 1), and indicated the nature of the bottom by abbreviations (also Fig 1) almost identical with those on Admiralty charts today.

After charting the Orkneys, he was commissioned by the Admiralty in 1751 to survey the West coast of Britain and the whole of the Irish coast. By 1757 the entire West coast of Scotland and its outlying islands had been completed on a scale of 1 in to the mile, and this chart, done in 1753, is an example of that work. With unflagging energy Murdoch Mackenzie carried on surveying, the results being gathered into the two-volume *A Maritim Survey of Ireland and the West of Great Britain*, published privately by Mackenzie in 1776. Among other achievements he read a paper to the Royal Society on the state of the tides in Orkney, produced a chart of the Atlantic Ocean on his own projection, and published *A Treatise on Maritim Surveying* (1774).

In 1771 he was succeeded as Admiralty Surveyor by his nephew, Murdoch Mackenzie, JUNIOR (1743–1829), with whom he is frequently confused.

Though both Murdoch Mackenzies were employed by the British Admiralty to carry out hydrographic surveys, the results of their labours were not published officially until after 1801.

## Bibliography

Robinson, 60–70, 165–6

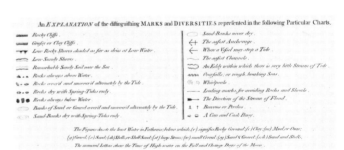

*Fig XLV–1.* Murdoch Mackenzie's signs and abbreviations. Compare with Fig XIV–1

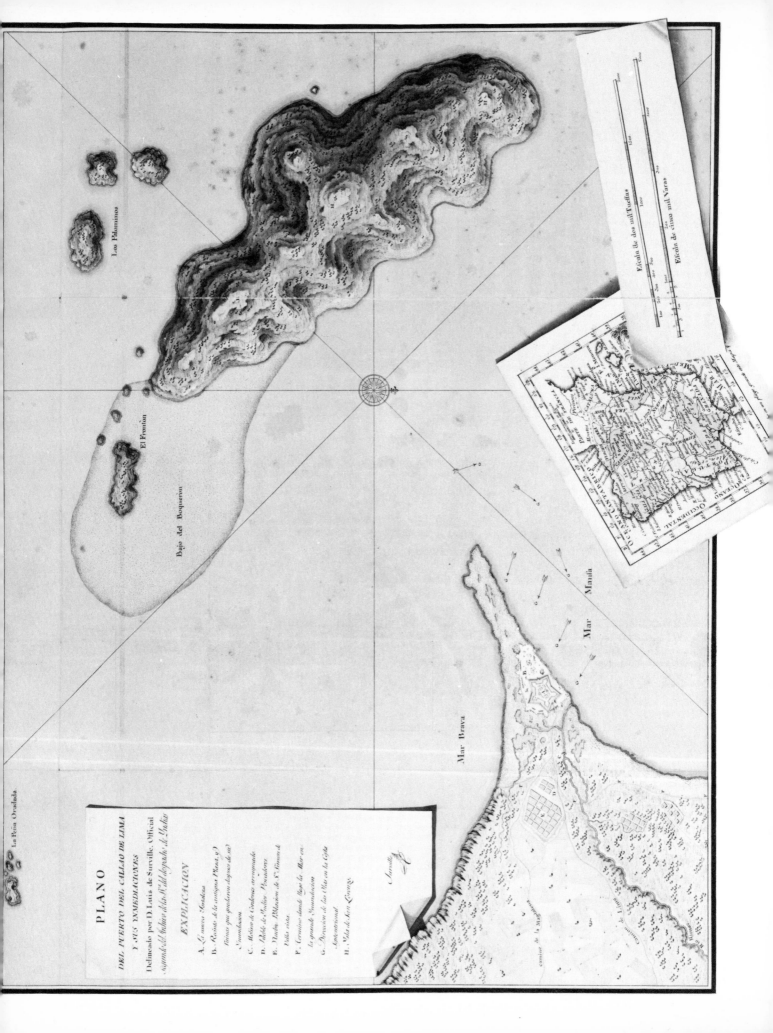

La Peña Oradada.

Los Palominos.

El Fronton

Bajo del Boqueron

Mar Brava

Mar Manña

Surville.

Camino de la Mag...

Escala de dos mil Tuellas

Escala de cinco mil Voras

OCEANO CANTABRICO

OCEANO OCCIDENTAL

**PLANO**

DEL PUERTO DEL CALLAO DE LIMA
Y SUS INMEDIACIONES

Delineado por D. Luis de Surville, Official
mayor del Archivo dela Scrã del Despacho de Indias

**EXPLICACION**

A. La nueva Fortaleza

B. Recinto de la antigua Plaza, y
ruinas que quedaron despues de su
Ynundacion.

C. Molino de Cordones arruinado.

D. Pueblo de Indios Pescadores.

E. Muelle, Poblacion de S.ᵗ Gerardo á
Vista vista.

F. Terrenos donde llego la Mar en
la grande Ynundacion.

G. Direccion de las Olas en la Costa
Accidental.

H. Yela de San Lorenzo.

# XLVI

# Callao, Peru

**Luis de Surville**

*[1778]*

1 : 32,000

PLANO DEL PUERTO DEL CALLAO DE LIMA Y SUS YNMEDIACIONES DELINEADO POR D. LUIS DE SURVILLE. OFFICIAL SEGUNDO DEL ARCHIVO DE LA SS<sup>a</sup> DEL DESPACHO DE YNDIAS [*Plan of the Port of Callao de Lima and its immediate surroundings. Drawn by Don Luis de Surville, second officer of the Record Office of the Indies*]. *Coloured plan,* MS *on paper, 405 × 465 mm. Plane projection, north at the bottom. From folio* MS *book* DESCRIPCION DE LA SITUACION DE LOS PUERTOS, ENSENADAS, CALETAS, Y SONDAS . . . SITUADOS EN LA AMERICA MERIDIONAL, CON SUS RESPECTIBOS PLANOS FORMADOS POR D. LUIS DE SURVILLE . . . AÑO DE 1778.

---

The manuscript plan opposite shows Callao, chief port of Peru, 7 miles west of the capital Lima, at that time the seat of the Spanish Viceroy. It was drawn about 1778 by a Spanish official of the Office of the Indies as one of the illustrations in a manuscript book reviewing the defences of ports and anchorages in Spanish Central and South America. Though Spain was at peace when the review was made, she became involved in the War of American Independence as an enemy of Britain the following year.

So far, Callao had successfully resisted foreign attack: the Dutch failed in 1624, and the English Commodore Anson was forced by scurvy to abandon an assault in 1741. This luck did not extend to natural disasters, however, for in 1746 an earthquake at sea raised an 80 ft wave that overwhelmed the town—the wave's direction is indicated here by arrows marked G, while the limit of the resulting flooding is marked F.

This plan has been chosen as an example of the superb draughtsmanship that characterised so many Spanish charts at this time (see also Chart XLIX). A particular feature of all the charts in de Surville's book is their realistic embellishment. One can almost feel the pins or wafers used to attach the various scraps of paper on which titles and scales are written; a sleepy fly has alighted on the border of the plan of Valdivia; and de Surville seems to have left a lottery ticket lying on the plan of Panama, a small map on the plan opposite, a hunting print on Payta, and a blue mezzotint on Cobija.

The book starts by describing Cartagena and Portobello on the Caribbean, then moves across the isthmus to the Pacific and deals with Panama Bay. De Surville then describes ports and anchorages in Ecuador, Peru, and Chile as far south as Chacao on the island of Chiloe, finishing with the various anchorages of the Juan Fernandez Islands.

On the title page of the book is a portrait that probably depicts de Surville himself. In the text, he refers to 'our published voyage', evidently a multi-volume work.

The units of distance on the bar-scales are the *tuessa*—equivalent to the French *toise*, just under 6 ft 4 in—and the *vara*, the Spanish yard, equivalent to 33 English in. No soundings are shown on the chart reproduced here but in the text and on other plans in the book soundings are in the *braza*, the Spanish fathom equivalent to the French *brasse* and the Italian *braccio*.

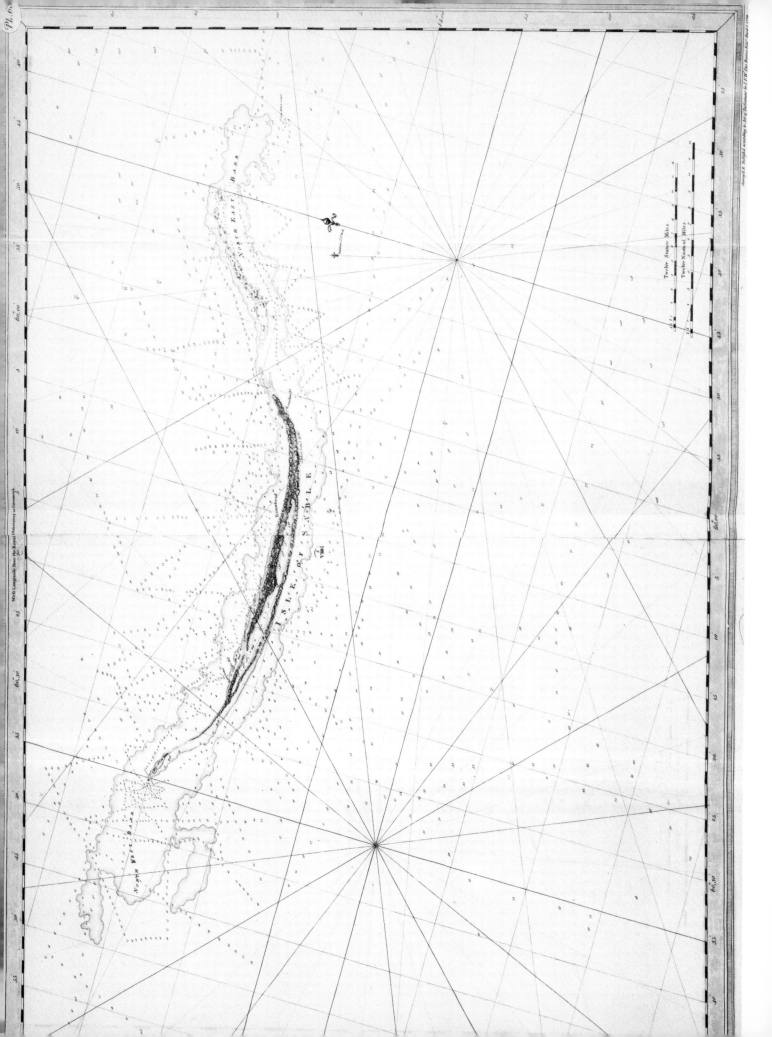

Pl. 68

ISLE OF SABLE

NORTH EAST BARR

NORTH WEST BARR

Twelve Statute Miles

Twelve Nautical Miles

# XLVII

## Sable Island, off Nova Scotia

### Joseph Frederick Wallet Des Barres

*1779*

## I : 120,000

THE ISLE OF SABLE . . . SURVEY'D & PUBLISH'D ACCORDING TO ACT OF PARLIAMENT BY I. F. W. DES BARRES ESQ. APRIL I. 1779. *Signed and dated. Chart on two sheets, engraved on Bates paper, 730 × 1,020 mm. Mercator's projection. Dated imprint at foot and numbered 'Pl. 63' at top right-hand corner of second sheet. From Des Barres'* THE ATLANTIC NEPTUNE PUBLISHED FOR THE USE OF THE ROYAL NAVY OF GREAT BRITAIN . . . *London, The Admiralty, [1784]. The Henry Newton Stevens Collection. In five parts. Separate titles to each; 26 preliminary leaves. Large Folio. 150 charts and views, with many states and variants of each.*

---

JOSEPH FREDERICK WALLET DES BARRES (1721–1824), who was of Swiss extraction, came to England as a young man, became a British subject and entered the Royal Military Academy, Woolwich. After completing his training as a military engineer, he was posted to North America, where he attracted the notice of General Wolfe and accompanied him as an engineer during the Quebec campaign.

After the fall of Quebec in 1759, Des Barres surveyed parts of the Nova Scotia coast, and in 1762 took part in Colonel Amherst's expedition to Newfoundland and surveyed several of its principal harbours. The following year Admiral Spry, the Commander-in-Chief on the North America station, told the Admiralty that the coasts of Nova Scotia and New England were very imperfectly charted and proposed that accurate surveys should be made. Des Barres was recommended for the task and sent to Halifax to make preparations.

Following ten years' arduous surveying, Des Barres returned to England in 1774, where the king ordered the publication of his findings; but the great work took another ten years before it was published, in 1784, under the title of *The Atlantic Neptune*. Its charts and views are divided into four distinct sections: *Nova Scotia, New England, Gulph and River of St Lawrence, and New York to the Gulph of Mexico.* The charts are remarkable for their wealth of accurate topographical detail, complemented by many finely engraved and coloured views, and served as the primary source for most American charts for the next fifty years.

Evidence of the difficulties and dangers Des Barres experienced are epitomised in this chart of Sable Island:

> . . . from 1763 to 1773, he was engaged in surveying the coast of Nova Scotia . . . two years were spent on the survey of the Isle of Sable alone. Two bars here, [The North East and North West

Barrs shewn on the chart] over which the surf broke often mast high, were strewn with wrecks for seven leagues, and could not be approached without the greatest risk. Des Barres completed the survey of the island and the soundings around it, at the hazard of his life.

Sable Island was and is, of course, a notorious navigational hazard—a long spit of shifting sand, swept by strong currents, lying directly across the approaches to Halifax, Nova Scotia.

This is the earliest chart in the book to show both true and magnetic meridians, and longitudes based on Greenwich, a result of the publication from 1767 on of *The Nautical Almanac*. This book simplified the calculations needed to find the longitude astronomically and gave results based on the meridian of the transit instrument in the Royal Observatory—longitude east or west of Greenwich.

Note also that Des Barres gives the Tidal Establishment (High Water Full and Change)—in this case, $VIII\frac{1}{2}^h$ (see Chart XVI).

### Bibliography

Evans, G. N. D. *Uncommon Obdurate—The several public careers of J. F. W. Des Barres* (Salem, Mass, 1969), 19

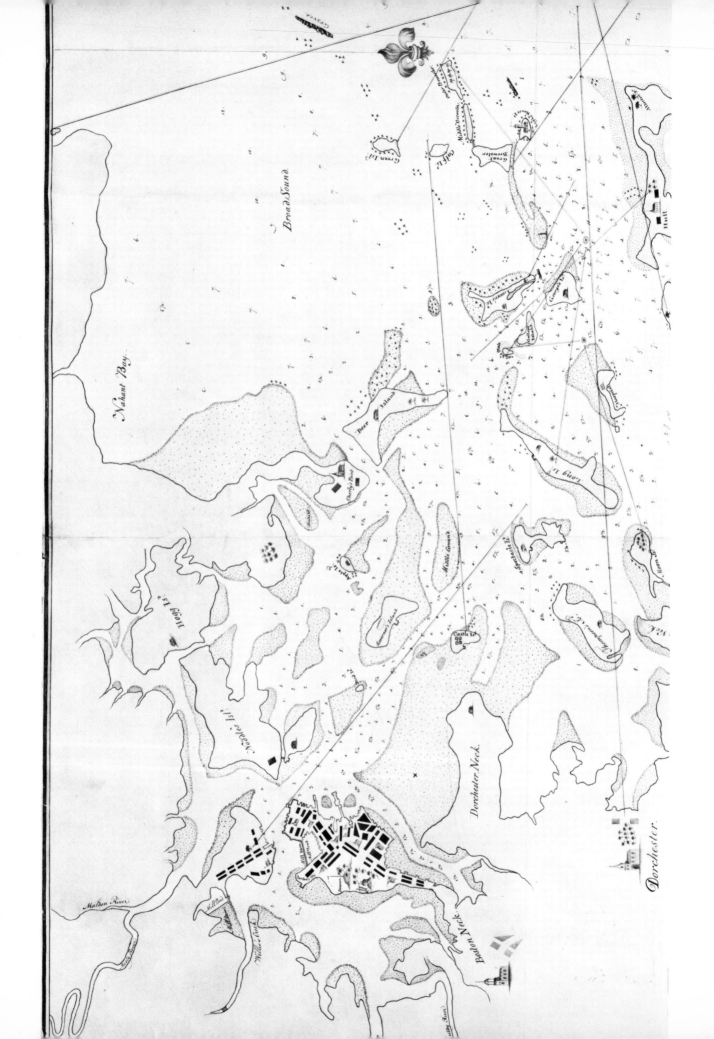

# XLVIII

# Boston, Massachusetts

[Emeric Vidal]

*c 1780*

1 : 26,000

*Detail from* A PLAN OF BOSTON HARBOUR. *Unsigned and undated. Hand-coloured* MS *chart on paper, 760 × 1,065 mm. Plane projection.*

---

This chart was probably copied from an original made about 1770. Many of the soundings are the same as those on Des Barres' chart of Boston, based on a survey of 1769.

Boston was at that time the principal seaport in America, and, judging from the number of soundings shown, was well surveyed. The straight lines over the sea, double red lines on the chart, are 'leading' and 'clearing' lines whose use in pilotage is best demonstrated by quoting from Des Barres' sailing directions:

To sail through the best Channel up to Boston    Sailing up to the Narrows, *keep the North Bluff of Hospital-Island a small Ship's Length open with the South Bluff of George's Island, till you bring a remarkable Hummock on the Land* (a little to the North Eastward of Boston) *open with the East Point of Nick's-Mate-Island.* Steer on these Marks as far up as Gallop Island; and thence, to avoid Nick's-Mate-Island and Lovell's-Island Shoals, keep Mid-Channel until you have Spectacle-Island entirely open with Long-Island Head. Then shape your Course between the North Point of Spectacle Island and Castle William Island, till you bring the first and second Church Steeples (from the North End of Boston) so near together that you can but just see Day-Light between them. When you are abreast of Castle William open gradually the Northmost Steeple (which is the highest) to the Eastward of the other; in order that by the Time you get the Meeting-House on Point Shirley, and the two Trees on the SW End of Governor's Island in One, the two Steeples may be a small Ship's Length asunder. —Thence bend gradually your Course to the Westward until the Northmost Steeple is almost shut in on the East Side of the other, and Anchor at Pleasure off the Long Wharf, in four or five Fathoms, Clay Bottom.

For those who know it today, the shape of the city is not easy to recognise due to the large amount of reclamation that has been carried out since 1770. *Noddles Island* has become East Boston; *Dorchester Neck* has become South Boston; *Governor's Island, Bird Island,* and *Apple Island* are all now part of Logan Airport; and *Castle Island* is now part of South Boston. The narrowest point of *Boston Neck,* the isthmus that was blocked during the siege of 1775–6, is at the intersection of Washington and Dover Streets; indeed, the *Neck* can hardly be identified on a modern map because filling in on both sides has made it part of the mainland. The islands in Boston Bay are, however, easier to identify, particularly *Lighthouse Island,* south of *Great Brewster:* the lighthouse shown here was built in 1716, destroyed in the Revolutionary War, and rebuilt in 1786. On the north bank of the Charles River, near the west border of the chart (omitted from the detail reproduced here), *The Colleges Cambridge* mark the position of Harvard University, founded in 1636.

This is one of a collection of charts made by VICE-ADMIRAL ROBERT DUFF (d 1787), who was Commander-in-Chief in Newfoundland from April 1775 until April 1776, during which time Boston was under siege by the revolutionary forces. He held the command in the Mediterranean from September 1777 to February 1780, during the Spanish siege of Gibraltar.

In the same collection is a chart of Gibraltar Bay, signed in the margin *E. Vidal del. 1780.* The Gibraltar chart is so similar in style and handwriting to the unsigned Boston chart reproduced here that they must both have been drawn by the same person.

EMERIC VIDAL first appears in the Admiralty muster lists as a volunteer landsman in the *Sylph* sloop in January 1777. A month later he transferred to the *Hector* as an AB. In March 1777 he joined Duff's Mediterranean flagship, the *Panther,* as an AB, being promoted to midshipman shortly after. When Duff returned to England in February 1780, Vidal transferred to the *Royal George* as a midshipman, becoming secretary to Duff's successor, Admiral John Lockhart Ross, in April 1780.

Vidal had three sons, all of whom joined the Royal Navy. The oldest was RICHARD EMERIC VIDAL (b 1789), who became a Commander; he was something of an artist and died in Canada. The middle son, EMERIC ESSEX VIDAL (d 1861), joined the Navy in 1806, becoming purser and paymaster; he was a distinguished painter, particularly of South American subjects and was present in St Helena when Napoleon was buried. He died in Brighton. The third son, ALEXANDER T. EMERIC VIDAL (d 1863, aged about seventy-three), became the distinguished hydrographic surveyor and the vice-admiral after whom HMS *Vidal,* a surveying ship in the Royal Navy today, is named.

The Vidal family originated in the Basque country on both sides of the Pyrenees and included many artists, whose talents Emeric Vidal and his sons certainly inherited.

## Bibliography

Admiralty Muster Lists
    PRO/ADM/36/8596–8—*Panther*
    PRO/ADM/36/8520–1—*Royal George*
Des Barres, J. F. W. *A Chart of the Harbour of Boston, composed from different surveys; but principally from that taken in 1769, by Mr. George Callendar, Late Master of His Majesty's Ship the Romney, Atlantic Neptune* (London, 5 August 1775)

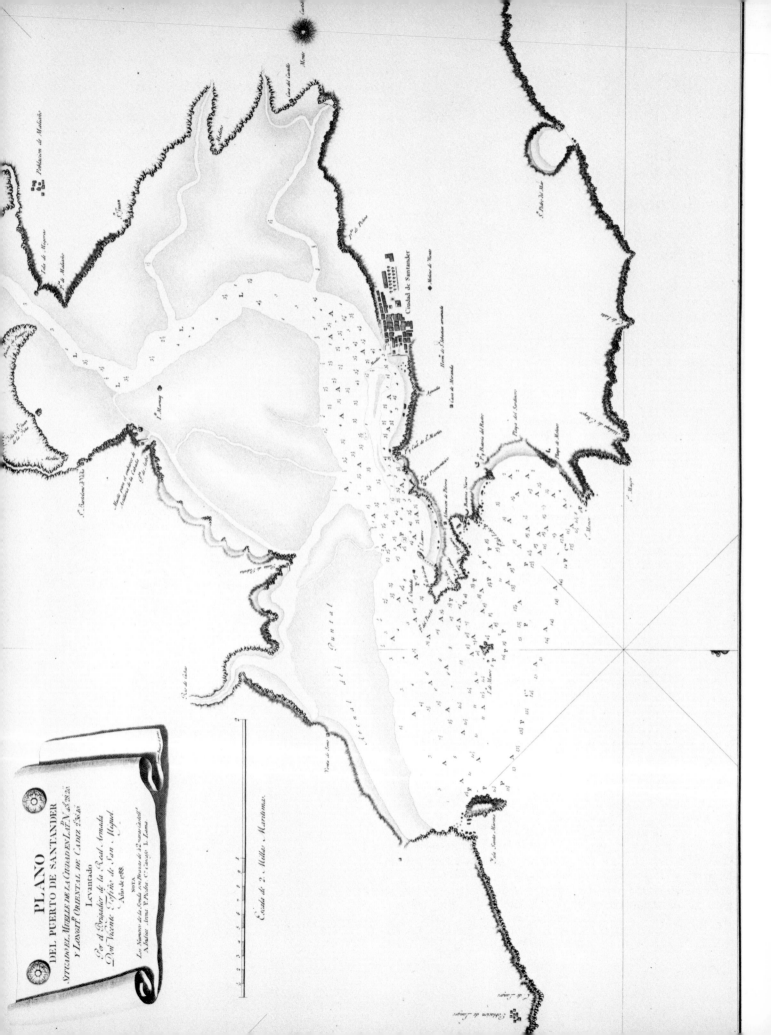

# PLANO
## DEL PUERTO DE SANTANDER

*Situado el Muelle de la Ciudad en Lat. N. de 43.° 28.′25.*
*y Longit. Oriental de Cadiz 2.° 8.′.40.*

### Levantado
*Por el Brigadier de la Real Armada*
*Don Vicente Tofiño de San Miguel.*
*Año de 1788.*

NOTA
*Los Numeros de la Sonda son Brazas de 2 varas castell.ᵃˢ*

Ciudad de Santander

Escala de 2. Millas Maritimas.

Arenal del Puntal

# XLIX

# Plan of the Port of Santander, Spain

## Don Vicente Tofiño de San Miguel

### 1778

### 1 : 24,600

PLANO DEL PUERTO DE SANTANDER, SITUADO EL MUELLE DE LA CIUDAD EN LAT.<sup>d</sup> N. 43° 28' 20'' Y LONGIT<sup>d</sup> ORIENTAL DE CADIZ 2° 36' 10''. LEVANTADO POR EL BRIGADIER DE LA REAL ARMADA DON VICENTE TOFIÑO DE SAN MIGUEL. AÑO DE 1788 [*Plan of the port of Santander, latitude (from the city centre) 43° 28' 20'' N., 2° 36' 10'' E of Cadiz. Drawn by . . . Don Vicente Tofiño de San Miguel. 1788*]. *Signed by Tofiño and also by the engraver, Joaquin Ballestir. Dated 1788. Plane chart, engraved on paper, 425 × 580 mm. Single cartouche. From the first volume of Tofiño's* ATLAS MARITIMO DE ESPAÑA. *Madrid, 1789. 2 volumes. Engraved titles to each; no text. Large Folio. 45 charts and views.*

---

Volume I of Tofiño's *Atlas Maritimo* contained charts and views of the Atlantic coast of Spain, Portugal, the Azores, and plans of the principal ports. The second volume covered the Mediterranean coast of Spain and the Balearics.

DON VICENTE TOFIÑO DE SAN MIGUEL (1732–95) is the best known Spanish marine cartographer. In addition to the *Atlas Maritimo*, he produced, c 1786, an atlas entitled *Cartas maritimas de la costa de España*. An English version of his plan of Cadiz harbour was published in London in 1805 by William Faden, and this was included in the sets of charts made up for ships of the Royal Navy as a result of the recommendations of the Chart Committee of the Admiralty (see Chart LI).

We have already mentioned the high quality of Spanish draughtmanship in this period, but the high quality of engraving is also notable in the Tofiño atlas. In this plan of the harbour of Santander, note the fine stippling of the sandbanks and delineation of the rocky coastline. Of great interest, too, is the use of letters to indicate the nature of the bottom found in the harbour estuary—and as auxiliary data to the soundings in fathoms (*brazas*):

A = Indica Arena = Sand
P = Piedra = Stones
C = Cascajo = Gravel
L = Lama = Mud, ooze

Though Murdoch Mackenzie, Senior, had used such abbreviations (see Chart LV), it was not till the 1820s that similar information began to appear on British Admiralty charts. The nature of the bottom was first written out in full—sand, rock, mud, etc—but abbreviations similar to Mackenzie's were used later.

Being a harbour plan, this chart is not graduated, but smaller-scale charts in the same atlas are on Mercator's projection. Various prime meridians are used, including Paris, Tenerife, Cadiz, and Ferrol.

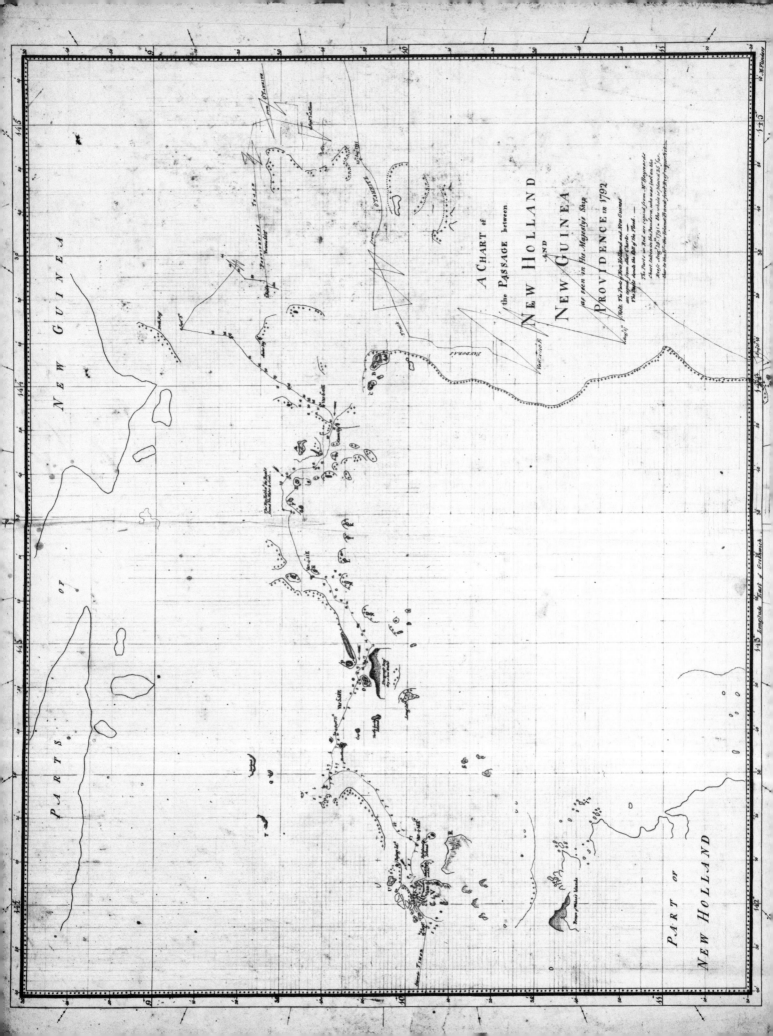

A CHART of
the PASSAGE between
NEW HOLLAND
AND
NEW GUINEA
as seen in His Majesty's Ship
PROVIDENCE in 1792

NEW GUINEA

PART of NEW HOLLAND

PARTS OF NEW GUINEA

L

# Torres Strait
## Matthew Flinders
*c 1792–1801*

*1 : 750,000*

A CHART OF THE PASSAGE BETWEEN NEW HOLLAND AND NEW GUINEA AS SEEN IN HIS MAJESTY'S SHIP PROVIDENCE IN 1792. *Signed M. Flinders. Undated* MS *Chart on paper, 460 × 575 mm. Mercator's projection.*

———

Thus was accomplished, in nineteen days, the passage from the Pacific, or Great Ocean, to the Indian Sea; without other misfortune than what arose from the attack of the natives, and some damage done to the cables and anchors. Perhaps no space of $3\frac{1}{2}°$ in length, presents more dangers than Torres' Strait; but, with caution and perseverence, the captains Bligh and Portlock proved them to be surmountable; and within a reasonable time: . . .

The subject of the above quotation was the passage of HM ships *Providence* and *Assistant* through the Torres Strait in 1792 during the second 'breadfruit voyage' of Captain William Bligh (1754–1817). The first breadfruit voyage had ended with the mutiny in the *Bounty*. In this second voyage, Bligh successfully transported 678 Pacific-grown plants to various West Indian islands in 1793. Sad to relate, in view of all the dramatic happenings connected with the project, the *Pandora*, sent to the South Pacific to hunt out the mutineers, was lost on a reef near the eastern entrance to the Torres Strait on the way home—in the end the West Indians apparently disliked the flavour of the breadfruit and preferred the plantain.

The chart reproduced opposite was drawn by MATTHEW FLINDERS (1774–1814), the main part of it probably under Bligh's supervision when Flinders was still a midshipman in the *Providence*. The quotation, from Flinders, was written many years after the events described, when he had become a captain and had passed through that same strait twice more.

In 1792 there had only been four passages through the Torres Strait between Australia and New Guinea—by Torres and Prado in 1606, by Cook in the *Endeavour* in 1770 (see Chart XLII), by Bligh in an open 23 ft launch after the mutiny on the *Bounty* in 1789, and by Captain Edward Edwards (1742–1815) and other survivors in HMS *Pandora*'s boats after her stranding in 1791. All were west-going passages, the winds and currents that prevail throughout the year in these dangerous waters making it very difficult for a sailing ship to make an easterly transit.

The original chart is drawn in two colours, the land and the October 1792 track of the *Providence* in black, and the 1791 track of the *Pandora* in red. The latter was 'copied from Mr. Hayward's Chart, taken in the *Pandora*, who was lost on the reefs August 29th, 1791', according to a note under the title (Hayward was a lieutenant in the *Pandora*).

Though there is not enough evidence to date this chart with certainty, it seems likely that Flinders drew the part in black in 1792 or 1793, and added the *Pandora*'s track in red later. It impinges on the black title, for one thing, and, for another, Flinders could not have known the details of the *Pandora*'s track until the *Providence* reached England in August 1793.

After his return home, Bligh sent to the Admiralty a chart of exactly the same area as the one here, without the *Pandora*'s track but with Cook's track of 1770 and his own boat passage of 1789. (*A Survey of the Straits between New Holland and New Guinea by Wm. Bligh.*) The detail from Flinders' chart is otherwise almost identical with Bligh's, including the designation of islands by the letters A, B, C, etc, one of Bligh's peculiarities. Flinders' version seen here (which has pencil squares for copying) has if anything slightly more detail, but it is not possible to tell which was copied from which.

Flinders almost certainly had the chart here with him during his survey of Australia in HMS *Investigator* from 1801 to 1803, and also during the six and a half trying years in Mauritius when he was a prisoner of war of the French. All the details on it were incorporated in the engraved chart that appeared as Plate XIII in the atlas published with his account of the voyage of the *Investigator*.

In the Royal Navy Flinders is perhaps best known for giving his name to the Flinders Bar, attached to a magnetic compass binnacle to correct for the effects of the soft iron in the ship's structure.

## Bibliography

Flinders, M. *A Voyage to Terra Australis . . . 1801, 1802 and 1803 in His Majesty's Ship the Investigator . . .* (1814), xxiv

Lee, Ida. *Captain Bligh's Second voyage to the South Sea* (1920), xi. Bligh's chart is reproduced facing p 178

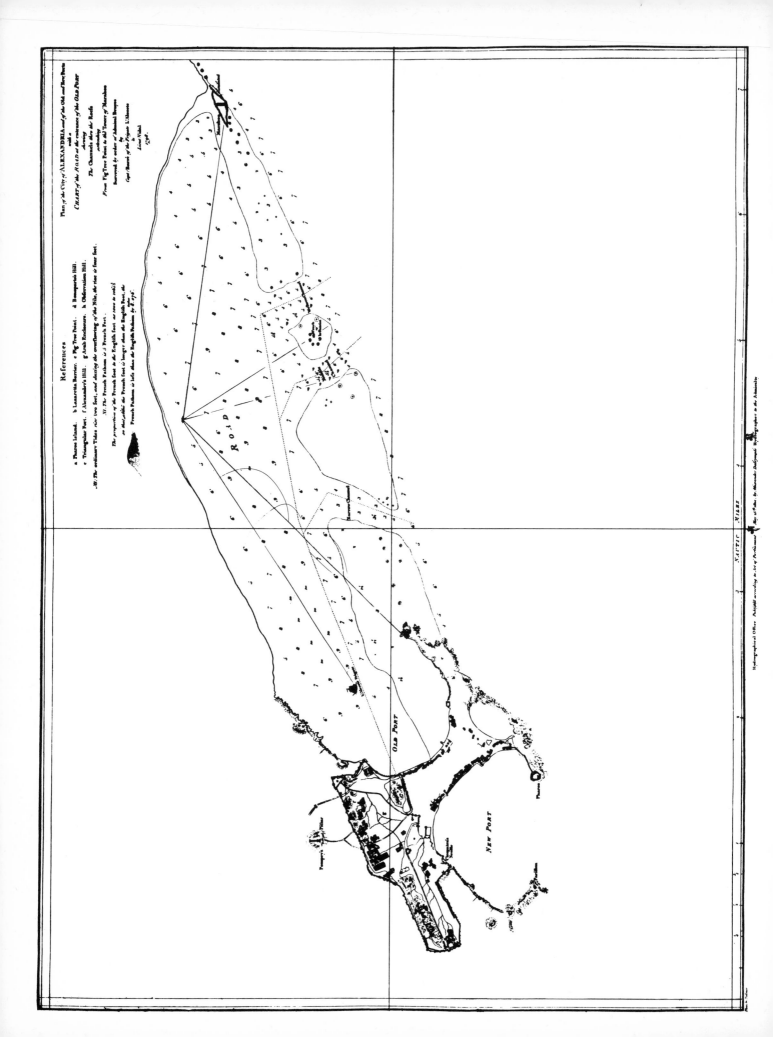

Plan of the City of ALEXANDRIA, and of the Old and New Ports

with a

CHART of the ROAD at the entrance of the OLD PORT

shewing

The Channels thro the Roads

extending

From Fig-Tree Point to th' Tower of Marabou

Surveyed by order of Admiral Bruyes

by

Capt Barré of the Frigate L'Alceste

Louis Vidal

1798

### References

a Pharos Island.    b Lazaretto Barrier.    e Fig-Tree Point.    d Bonaparte's Hill.

e Triangular Fort.    f Alexander's Hill.    g Arab Enclosure.    h Observation Hill.

i French Fort.

N: The ordinary Tides rise two feet, and during the overflowing of the Nile, the rise is four feet.

M: The French Fathom is to the English foot as two to nine.

The proportion of the French foot to the English foot, as twelve to eleven; that while the French foot is longer than the English foot, the French Fathom is less than the English Fathom by two feet.

ROAD

NAUTIC MILES

OLD PORT

NEW PORT

Pharos

Hydrographical Office. Published according to Act of Parliament, May 18. 1801, by Alexander Dalrymple Hydrographer to the Admiralty

# LI

# Alexandria, Egypt
## British Admiralty
### 1801

### 1 : 23,500

PLAN OF THE CITY OF ALEXANDRIA AND OF THE OLD AND NEW PORTS WITH A CHART OF THE ROAD . . . SURVEYED BY ORDER OF ADMIRAL BRUYES BY CAPT: BARRÉ OF THE FRIGATE L'ALCESTE & LIEUT: VIDAL 1798. HYDROGRAPHICAL OFFICE. PUBLISHED ACCORDING TO ACT OF PARLIAMENT MAY 25TH 1801 BY ALEXANDER DALRYMPLE HYDROGRAPHER TO THE ADMIRALTY. *Engraved on paper by Palmer (plan) and Harmer (writing), 470 × 630 mm. Plane projection, north at the bottom.*

---

ALEXANDER DALRYMPLE, 'Hydrographer to the Admiralty', published the two earliest Admiralty Charts on 25 May 1801: one, *Chart of the Coast of Egypt From the Western Mouth of the Nile to the Tower of the Arabs. Laid down from various materials and observations in H.M. Ships on that station;* the other, *Plan of the City of Alexandria . . .*, reproduced opposite.

When these charts were published in 1801, Egypt was under French occupation. Only two months earlier, however, British forces had landed in Aboukir Bay, where Nelson had destroyed the French Fleet in the Battle of the Nile in 1798, and details of these landings are given on the coastal chart. The plan of Alexandria opposite is based upon a captured French chart, the story of whose capture is told in a note on a manuscript copy of the same chart also in the Museum's collection, and acquired, incidentally, from an entirely different source.

When the French fleet reached Egypt in 1798, Admiral Bruyes was advised, contrary to what he had heard, that the Old Port at Alexandria was not suitable for large ships. Despite the offer of a reward of 10,000 livres, no native pilot would take a ship in if she was drawing more than 20 ft. 'It is vexatious that there is not a Port where the Fleet can enter', Bruyes said, and thereupon ordered Captain Barré and First-Lieutenant Citizen Vidal (no relation to the distinguished British hydrographic surveyor of the same name) of the frigate *Alceste* to find a channel. They carried out a survey accordingly.

On 19 June 1799 three French frigates and two brigs sailing from Jaffa to Toulon, including the *Alceste*, with Barré in command, and *La Courageuse* with Vidal and the plan of Alexandria on board, were captured by a British squadron about 20 leagues south of Toulon. A copy of the Alexandria plan was sent by the *Centaur* to Dalrymple in London who published it virtually without amendment—though upside down—leaving the soundings in French fathoms but adding a note to the printed chart giving the equivalent in English units—a fraction under 5ft 4in.

The printed chart reproduced opposite has no compass rose, but points of the compass are shown (with true north at the bottom) round the outside borders of the chart. Being a plan, it is not graduated for latitude and longitude, though its companion coastal chart is.

On the back is written in ink 'Sir T. Troubridge', apparently in his own hand. Troubridge (1758–1807) had been one of Nelson's captains—one of his 'band of brothers'—and was a Lord Commissioner of the Admiralty at the time of publication. The Museum's copy of the captured French chart comes from the collection of Admiral Sir J. T. Duckworth (1748–1817), Rear-Admiral of the White under Lord St Vincent in the Mediterranean at the time of the capture.

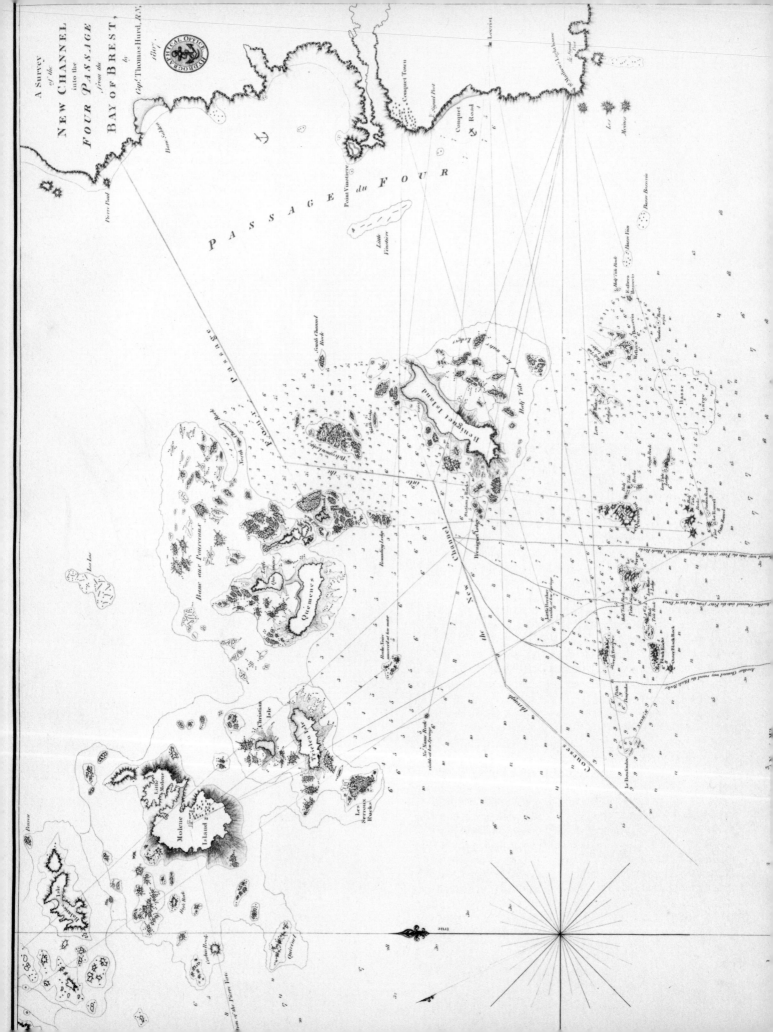

# LII

# *The Approaches to the Harbour of Brest, Brittany*

## British Admiralty (*Captain* Thomas Hurd, RN)

## *1807*

## I : 33,000

A SURVEY OF THE NEW CHANNEL INTO THE FOUR PASSAGE FROM THE BAY OF BREST, BY CAPT. THOMAS HURD, R.N., 1807. *Signed Hurd. Dated 1807. Plane chart, engraved on paper, 455 × 610 mm. With Admiralty 'Hydrographical Office' device. Imprint (at foot):* HYDROGRAPHICAL OFFICE. PUBLISHED ACCORDING TO ACT OF PARLIAMENT 12TH APRIL 1809, BY CAPT. HURD, R.N. HYDROGRAPHER TO THE ADMIRALTY. *From Hurd's atlas* CHARTS OF THE ENGLISH CHANNEL . . . *London, Ballintine & Byworth, 1811. Printed title; table of contents; no text. Large Folio. 31 charts.*

---

The chart opposite was the direct result of the wreck of one of HM ships. In March 1804 Admiral Cornwallis, commanding the British squadron blockading Brest, reported that HMS *Magnificent* had been lost on a sunken rock not marked on British charts, though it was subsequently found under the name *Le Boufouloc* (Buffalo) on the appropriate chart in *Le Neptune François* (see Chart XLIII).

As a result, the Admiralty sent Captain Thomas Hurd to carry out hydrographic surveys off Brest; and he started in June 1804 under war conditions off an enemy coast, almost all the surveying being done in two six-oared cutters. Hurd produced two charts of the Brest area, one of which is reproduced here. They were the first British Admiralty charts to be published after Hurd became Hydrographer to the Admiralty in 1808 (the term Hydrographer of the Navy was not then used) and two of the earliest to show the 'Hydrographical Office' device (below the title here).

*Le Boufouloc* is close to the outer end of Hurd's new channel at bottom left.

CAPTAIN THOMAS HURD, RN (1757?–1823), served with distinction in the Royal Navy during the American War of Independence and was present at the action off Dominica on 9 April 1782. He learned his surveying with Samuel Holland and J. F. W. Des Barres in North America, and, while in the West Indies, carried out the first exact survey of Bermuda. In May 1808 he succeeded Alexander Dalrymple as Hydrographer to the Admiralty, a post which he held until his death. Before then he had been a member of the Admiralty Chart Committee that recommended which privately published charts should be supplied to the Fleet. During his term of office, the RN surveying service was placed under his control, and he also became Secretary to the Board of Longitude. It was due to his efforts that

British Admiralty charts were first placed on public sale in 1823.

In 1811 his *Charts of the English Channel* . . . (thirty-one charts), whence this chart comes, was published, and also a companion atlas, *Charts of the coasts of France, Spain & Portugal, from Brest to Gibraltar*; forming volume II of the Channel Atlas. Hurd included not only his own charts in these atlases, but others by colleagues in the Hydrographical Office and also a number by French hydrographers. A few of them were printed from privately published plates—some endorsed 'Approved by the Chart Committee of the Admiralty', some merely rubber stamped 'Hydrographical Office'.

## Bibliography

Leyland, J. (ed). *Dispatches and Letters relative to the Blockade of Brest 1803–1805*, 2 vols (Navy Records Society, 1899), i, 299, 306–9, 319; ii, 52

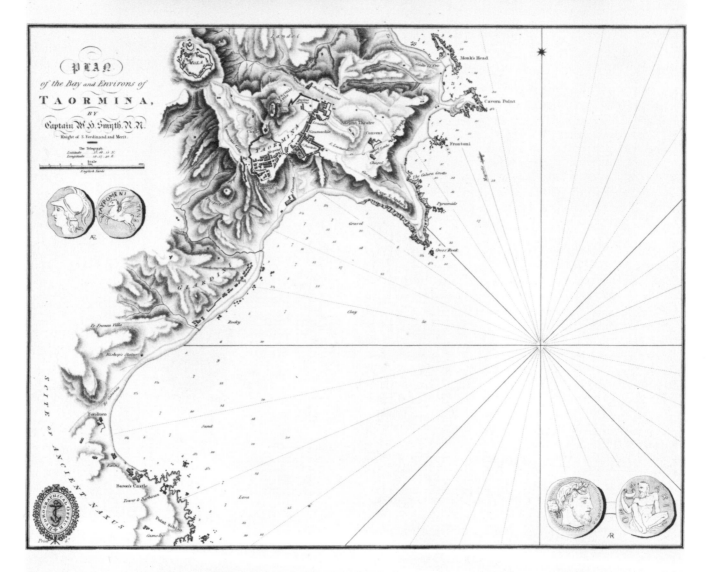

PLAN
of the Bay and Environs of
TAORMINA,
BY
Captain W. H. Smyth, R.N.
Knight of S. Ferdinand and Merit.

VIEW OF SCHISO POINT.

London Published according to Act of Parliament at the Hydrographical Office of the Admiralty 19th July 1823.

# LIII

# Taormina, Sicily

## British Admiralty (*Captain*, later *Admiral*, William Henry Smyth)

### *1823*

### 1 : 20,000

[1]. VIEW OF THE CITY OF TAORMINA. [2] PLAN OF THE BAY AND ENVIRONS OF TAORMINA, BY CAPTAIN W. H. SMYTH, R.N. . . . [3]. VIEW OF SCHISO POINT. *Signed Smyth. Dated 1823. Plan and two views, engraved on paper ; sheet size 500 × 360 mm. Imprint (at foot) :* LONDON. PUBLISHED ACCORDING TO ACT OF PARLIAMENT AT THE HYDROGRAPHICAL OFFICE OF THE ADMIRALTY 19TH JULY 1823. *From Smyth's atlas :* THE HYDROGRAPHY OF SICILY, MALTA, AND THE ADJACENT ISLANDS . . . *Printed title ; table of contents ; no text. Folio. 32 charts, plans and engraved views.*

---

In an active naval career ADMIRAL SMYTH (1788–1865) saw service in the East Indies, Europe, and the Mediterranean, during which he took part in the Scheldt expedition (1808–9) and operations off the Spanish coast (1810–12). Between 1813 and 1823 he conducted a detailed hydrographic survey of Sicily, the adjacent coasts of Italy and parts of North Africa and Greece. The result of this work was a number of finely engraved charts and views published by the Admiralty. Shortly afterwards Smyth published his *Memoir . . . of the resources, inhabitants and hydrography of Sicily and its islands* (1824) and four years later his *Sketch of Sardinia.*

The period immediately after a war is frequently very productive of good hydrographic surveys, as Smyth proved. Many of his young officers made names for themselves later, particularly in South America in Smyth's own ship, HMS *Adventure.*

At the end of his service at sea in 1824 Smyth turned to literary and scientific pursuits, becoming a Fellow of the Royal Society in 1826 and, in 1830, one of the Founders of the Royal Geographical Society. In later life he was President of both the Royal Astronomical and Royal Geographical Societies. He built an astronomical observatory at his home near Bedford and wrote many books on a variety of topics, including the well known nautical dictionary *The Sailors Word-Book.*

Smyth's plan and views of Taormina illustrate both the high quality of the engraving, pictorially and cartographically, and his antiquarian interests, as shown in the attractive representation of the obverse and reverse of two Greek coins. Note also that British Admiralty charts have now begun to show the nature of the bottom—sand, lava, rocky, gravel, clay—though not yet in abbreviated form.

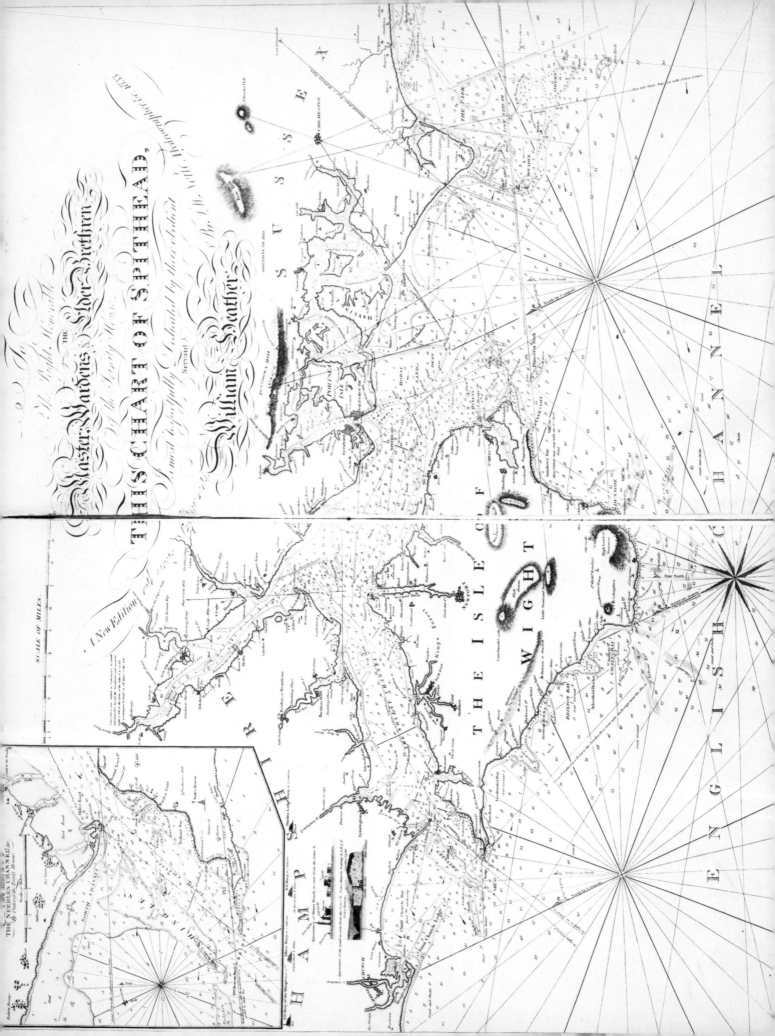

# LIV

## The Solent and Spithead, and, inset, The Needles Channel

### William Heather, revised by John William Norie

*1833*

## I : 100,000

TO THE RIGHT HONORABLE THE MASTER, WARDENS & ELDER BRETHREN OF THE TRINITY HOUSE, THIS CHART OF SPITHEAD, IS MOST RESPECTFULLY DEDICATED BY THEIR OBEDIENT SERVANT, WILLIAM HEATHER. A NEW EDITION WITH VARIOUS IMPROVEMENTS, BY J. W. NORIE, HYDROGRAPHER, &C. 1833. ADDITIONS TO 1835. INSET: A NEW SURVEY OF THE NEEDLES CHANNEL &C. BY ORDER OF THE TRINITY HOUSE. *Signed Heather & Norie. Dated 1833. Plane chart, with inset, engraved on paper, 630 × 770 mm. Imprint (at foot):* RE-PUBLISHED, AS THE ACT DIRECTS, AUGUST 1ST, 1833., BY J. W. NORIE & CO. (SUCCESSORS TO THE LATE WILLIAM HEATHER) NO. 157 LEADENHALL STREET, LONDON. *From Heather & Norie's* THE COMPLETE BRITISH AND IRISH COASTING PILOT . . . *London, J. W. Norie, [1835]. Printed title; table of contents; no text. Large Folio. 16 charts.*

---

The last three charts reproduced have been official British Admiralty publications, but here is an example of the privately published British chart, which came to be called the 'blue-back' (see Chart LVI).

In 1765 WILLIAM HEATHER (fl 1740–1812) set up as a publisher and dealer in charts and nautical instruments at 157 Leadenhall Street, London, under the sign of the 'Little Midshipman'. For the next forty or so years he produced a series of important charts and pilot-guides, including *A Pilot for the Atlantic Ocean* (1795–1801), charts of the Channel (1801), pilots for the Mediterranean and East Indies (1802–5), and the *Marine Atlas or Seaman's Complete Pilot* (1808).

After his death in 1812 the business was taken over by the celebrated hydrographer and nautical instructor John William Norie (1772–1843), best known for his *Epitome of Practical Navigation* (1805), which remained a standard work for many years, and the *Complete Set of Nautical Tables* (1803). He continued Heather's work by publishing new editions of his pilots, with the charts revised and brought up-to-date. Norie retired about 1830 but the business was carried on in Leadenhall Street until 1880, when it removed to the Minories.

This chart of the Solent and Spithead is typical of the output of this firm, showing the revised material by Norie incorporated into the original chart by Heather. Cartographically, note the delightful engraving of coastline views (eg, 'Appearance of Hurst Beach . . .'), the representation of buoys, and the interesting method used to depict the tidal races and overfalls off the south coast of the Isle of Wight.

The florid title is typical of the privately published chart of this period, in contrast to its more sober Admiralty counterpart. Furthermore, it still has the network of rhumbs (descending directly from the portulan chart), already generally abandoned in Admiralty charts in favour of compass roses.

The fact that this 1833 chart should have the legend 'Additions to 1835' is significant, showing a growing awareness of the need to keep charts up-to-date. On the initiative of the newly appointed Hydrographer of the Navy, Francis Beaufort, the *Nautical Magazine* was started in 1832 specifically to give information for the correction of charts. In 1834 this function was taken over by *Admiralty Notices to Mariners*, still issued today.

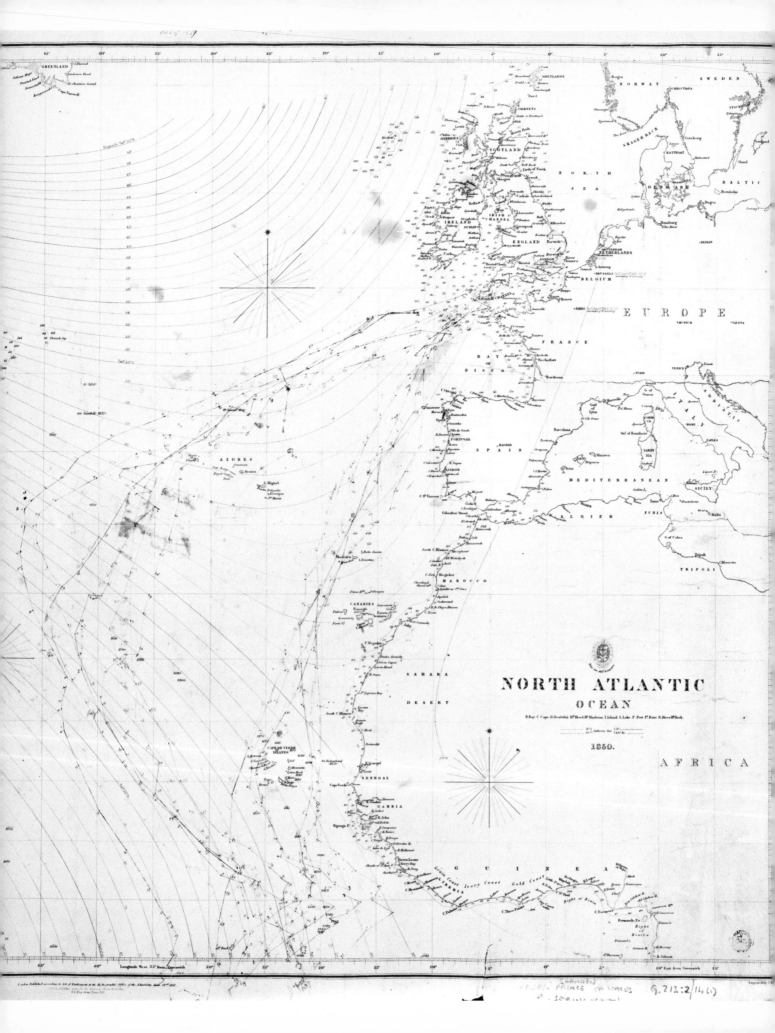

# NORTH ATLANTIC

## OCEAN

B.Bay. C.Cape. D.Doubtful. H⁴ Head. H⁺ Harbour. I.Island. L.Lake. P. Port. P⁴ Point. R.River. R⁴ Rock.

1859.

EUROPE

AFRICA

# North Atlantic Ocean

**British Admiralty No 2053, with MS additions**

*1851*

**I : II,400,000 (40° N)**

*Eastern half of* NORTH ATLANTIC OCEAN 1850. LONDON. PUBLISHED . . . AT THE HYDROGRAPHIC OFFICE OF THE ADMIRALTY JUNE 23RD 1851. *Engraved on paper by J. & C. Walker*, 631 × 945 *mm. Mercator's projection.*

The main interest here stems not from the printed chart but from the manuscript additions—from the tracks, variously dated between 1851 and 1868, of five 'Blackwall frigates'.

As the name implies, Blackwall frigates were wooden ships built on naval lines, mostly at Blackwall on the north bank of the River Thames, a few miles below London Bridge. Basil Lubbock has said of them: 'The Blackwall frigates form a connecting link between the lordly East Indiaman of the Honourable John Company and the magnificent P. & O. and Orient liners of the present day'. From 1840 to 1870 they were the leaders in the East India passenger trade to India, China and, latterly, Australia.

All the tracks on this chart refer to ships belonging to Messrs R. & H. Green of Blackwall, and all but one were built in the Blackwall yard. The earliest ship represented is the *Seringapatam*, 818 tons, built in 1837 and the first of the Blackwall frigates; there are outward tracks for 1851, homeward for 1853.

Next comes the *Prince of Wales*, 1,223 tons, built in 1842, with outward tracks for 1854 and 1855, and homeward for 1855 and 1856; 'D.C.', probably the *Dover Castle*, 1,002 tons, built in Sunderland to Blackwall lines in 1858, with homeward track for 1863; the *Shannon*, 1,292 tons, built in 1862, the first with iron beams, with 1866 homeward track; and finally the *Agamemnon*, 1,431 tons and 252 ft in length, the largest ship to be built by Green's in the Blackwall yard, in 1855—homeward-bound 1868.

The tracks demonstrate the routes taken by sailing ships in the Atlantic, routes dictated by the prevailing winds and currents. Outward-bound from the Channel to the Cape of Good Hope, ships would sail direct for Madeira, keep fairly close to the African coast to take advantage of the favourable current until about 5° N, and turn west and south with the North-east Trades across to the coast of South America into the Brazil current until the Roaring Forties took them back across the South Atlantic towards the Cape of Good Hope. Homeward-bound ships would sail from the Cape past St Helena and Ascension until they picked up the North-east Trades, strike north and west to mid-Atlantic, then turn towards the Channel with the Gulf Stream and North-Atlantic Drift Current behind them.

This is a good example of a mid-century small-scale chart. Deep-sea soundings are few and far between, data for these not being obtainable until the surveys connected with the laying of the Atlantic cable and until the epic voyage of HMS *Challenger* in the 1860s and 1870s. Note the lines of equal magnetic variation presented in much the same way as Halley had presented his results of 1698–1700 (see Chart XXXIII).

At this time it was Admiralty practice not to include the Hydrographer's name in the imprint of the chart but to insert his initials in the Hydrographic Office seal—in this case 'F.B.' for Rear-Admiral Sir Francis Beaufort (1774–1857), Britain's most distinguished nineteenth-century Hydrographer of the Navy. During his term of office the number of charts in the Admiralty list rose from 852 in 1829 to over 2,000 in 1855. Beaufort's name is best known for his scale for estimating the wind force visually, a scale still in worldwide use today.

## Bibliography

Lubbock, B. *The Blackwall Frigates* (Glasgow, 1922)

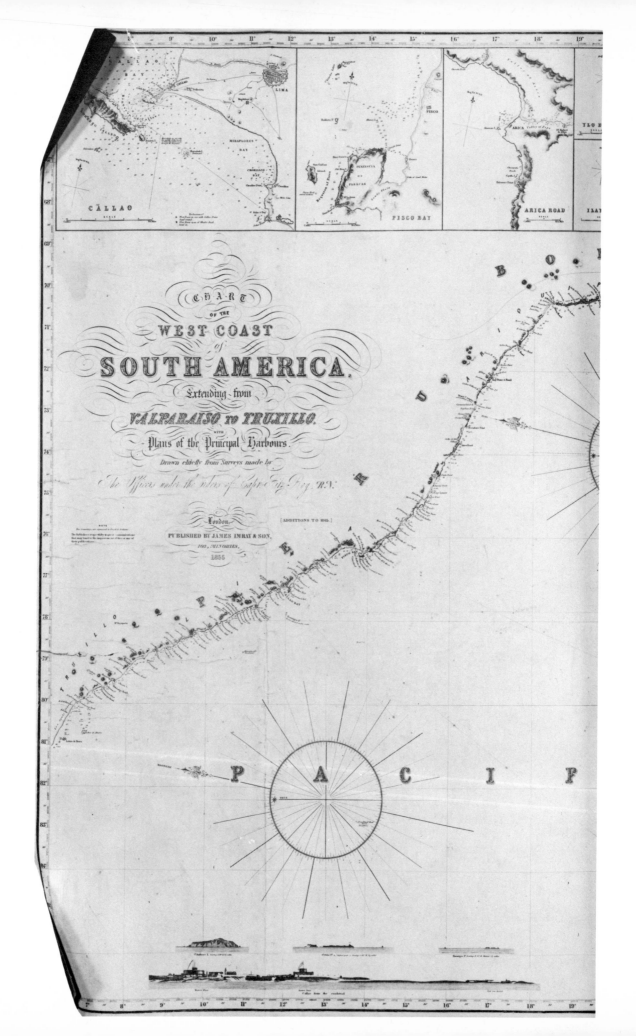

CALLAO

FISCO BAY

ARICA ROAD

ILAY

CHART
OF THE
WEST COAST
of
SOUTH AMERICA,
Extending from
VALPARAISO TO TRUXILLO,
WITH
Plans of the Principal Harbours.

Drawn chiefly from Surveys made by
The Officers under the orders of Capt. Fitz Roy, R.N.

London,
[ADDITIONS TO 1865.]
PUBLISHED BY JAMES IMRAY & SON,
102, MINORIES,
1855

PACIF

# LVI

# Coast of Peru
## James Imray & Son
### *1855 [corrected to 1865]*
### 1 : 2,640,000 (20° S)

*Northern part of* CHART OF THE WEST COAST OF SOUTH AMERICA
EXTENDING FROM VALPARAISO TO TRUXILLO WITH PLANS OF THE
PRINCIPAL HARBOURS. DRAWN CHIEFLY FROM SURVEYS MADE BY
THE OFFICERS UNDER THE ORDERS OF CAPT. FITZROY R.N. LONDON,
PUBLISHED BY JAMES IMRAY & SON, 102 MINORIES, 1855 [ADDI-
TIONS TO 1865]. *Engraved on paper, mounted on blue backing
paper, 1,000 × 1,300 mm. Mercator's projection, north to the left.*

---

Though British Admiralty charts were put on sale in 1823,
private chart publishers continued to hold a considerable share
of the market during the nineteenth century, though sales had
dwindled very considerably by the 1880s. The chart opposite is
an example of such a privately published chart, known, for
reasons which will become clear, as a 'blueback'.

In the late eighteenth and early nineteenth centuries most
charts could be bought either in sets bound up into atlases, or in
sheet form, often supplied rolled. Because of the greater wear
and tear suffered by the latter, they were often mounted on some
form of backing—occasionally light canvas or linen, more often
one or more sheets of tough paper, the outer one of which was
usually blue. The earliest blueback in the Museum's collection
was printed about 1760—a chart of the New England coast that
appeared also (unmounted) in various editions of Mount &
Page's *The English Pilot—The Fourth Book* between 1765 and
1770.

During the early nineteenth century, as the popularity of the
sea atlas waned, so the rolled blueback chart developed along its
own lines, becoming the generic term for the privately published
British chart used by merchant ships. It tended to become
longer, often well over 6 ft, and, to cut down the number of
charts required by any one ship, the small-scale charts had many
port plans shown as insets. The chart opposite is a mid-nine-
teenth-century blueback, smaller than some, being less than
5 ft long. About half the chart is rolled up in the illustration.

The area shown is the Pacific coast of America, and pencil
tracks dated 1873 to and from Callao can be seen. The plan of
Callao at top left should be compared with de Surville's manuscript plan of 1778 (XLVI).

Though bluebacks were published privately, the cartographic
and hydrographic data was obtained almost exclusively from
official sources—in this case from the surveys of Captain Robert
Fitzroy (1805–65) and the officers of HMS *Beagle* between 1831
and 1836, surveys which opened up South America to European

trade, and which are best known because of the writings of the
*Beagle*'s naturalist, Charles Darwin—*The Voyage of the Beagle*
and *On the Origin of the Species* . . .

The firm of James Imray & Son was descended from that of
John Hamilton Moore (author of *The Practical Navigator*)
established in 1763. It became Blachford in 1801, Blachford &
Imray in 1836, J. Imray in 1840, and Imray & Son before 1855.
In 1899, the Imrays joined with the firm of Norie & Wilson—
successors of William Heather (see Chart LIV), who had first
published John Norie's *Nautical Tables* and *Epitome of Navigation* in 1803.

In 1903 Laurie's, the only other publishers of bluebacks (who
claimed descent from John Seller, see Charts XXV and XXVI,
and Sayer & Bennett, see Chart XXXVII), joined with the
others to form Imray, Laurie, Norie, and Wilson, Ltd, still in
existence today. Since 1950 the firm has ceased to maintain a
world list of charts and has concentrated on specialised charts,
such as those for fishermen and yachtsmen, and on charts of
UK home waters.

### Bibliography

Luymes, J. 'The Blueback', *International Hydrographic Review*,
viii (1931), 33
Wilson, Elena. *The Story of the Blueback Chart* (1937)

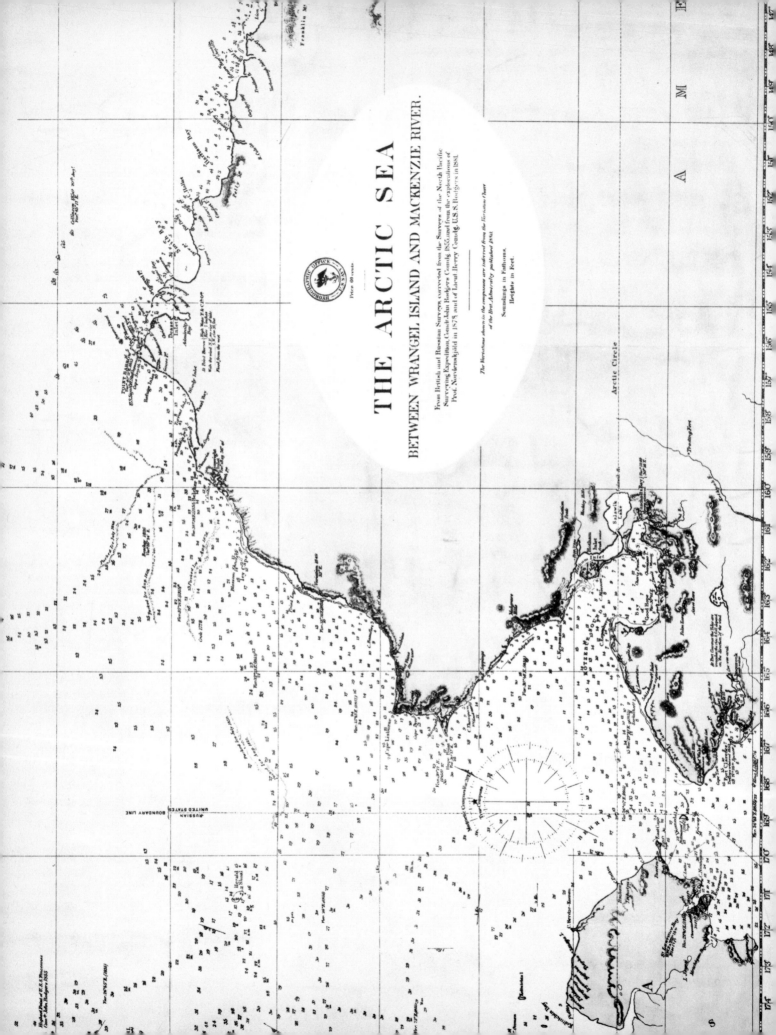

# THE ARCTIC SEA

## BETWEEN WRANGEL ISLAND AND MACKENZIE RIVER.

From British and Russian Surveys, corrected from the Surveys of the North Pacific Surveying Expedition, Comr. John Rodgers Comdg. 1855, and from the explorations of Prof. Nordenskjöld in 1879 and of Lieut. Berry Comdg. U.S.S. Rodgers in 1881.

The Variations shown in the compasses are inferred from the Variation Chart of the Brit. Admiralty published 1881.

Soundings in Fathoms.

Heights in Feet.

Price 60 cents.

# LVII

# Arctic Coasts of Russia and Alaska

## US Hydrographic Office No 912
## 1882
## 1 : 2,000,000 (71° 30′ N)

*South-west part of* THE ARCTIC SEA BETWEEN WRANGEL ISLAND AND MACKENZIE RIVER . . . PUBLISHED FEB^y 1882 AT THE HYDROGRAPHIC OFFICE WASHINGTON D.C. . . . *Coloured chart, lithograph on paper, 615 × 1,055 mm. Mercator's projection.*

---

As explained in the Introduction, United States charts are produced by two separate agencies according to whether the area shown is at home or abroad. The chart opposite, a painstaking compilation from many US, British, Swedish, and Russian sources, was published in 1882 by the US Hydrographic Office.

The chart includes the results of exploration on the Siberian coast in 1878 by A. E. Nordenskiöld (1832–1901), the Swedish polar explorer and historian of cartography. The north Alaskan shore shows *Icy Cape*, furthest point reached by Cook in 1778. It also shows *Point Barrow* (named after the then second secretary of the British Admiralty), where T. Elson, Master, and his crew, sailing north-east up the coast in the barge from HMS *Blossom* (Captain F. W. Beechey), were forced to turn back in August 1826; and *Return Reef*, furthest point reached that same month by John Franklin (1786–1847) and his two boats, sailing westwards from the Mackenzie River to meet the *Blossom*'s boats sailing eastwards from the Bering Strait. Alas! sea-ice conditions that August forced both parties to turn back while they were still over 140 nautical miles apart. Cook, Beechey, Franklin, Belcher, McClure, Collinson, Rodgers, Nordenskiöld, Berry—all these explorers' names can be seen on this chart among the magnetic and tidal information, in the notes on ice conditions, or among the soundings and placenames.

US charts from both the US Hydrographic Office (USHO) and the US Coast and Geodetic Survey (USCGS) were notable for their technical innovations. For example, this is the earliest chart in this book to have been printed by photolithography, though the basis was probably an engraved copperplate; and it is the first to make use of colour printing, the land having a buff tint.

Two other points are worth noting: the large magnetic variations given, due to the fact that the area portrayed is not far from the North Magnetic Pole; and the longitude scales based on Greenwich. Following in the steps of Des Barres' *Atlantic Neptune* (Chart XLVII), almost all US charts were based on Greenwich even before it was chosen internationally in 1884 as the world's prime meridian.

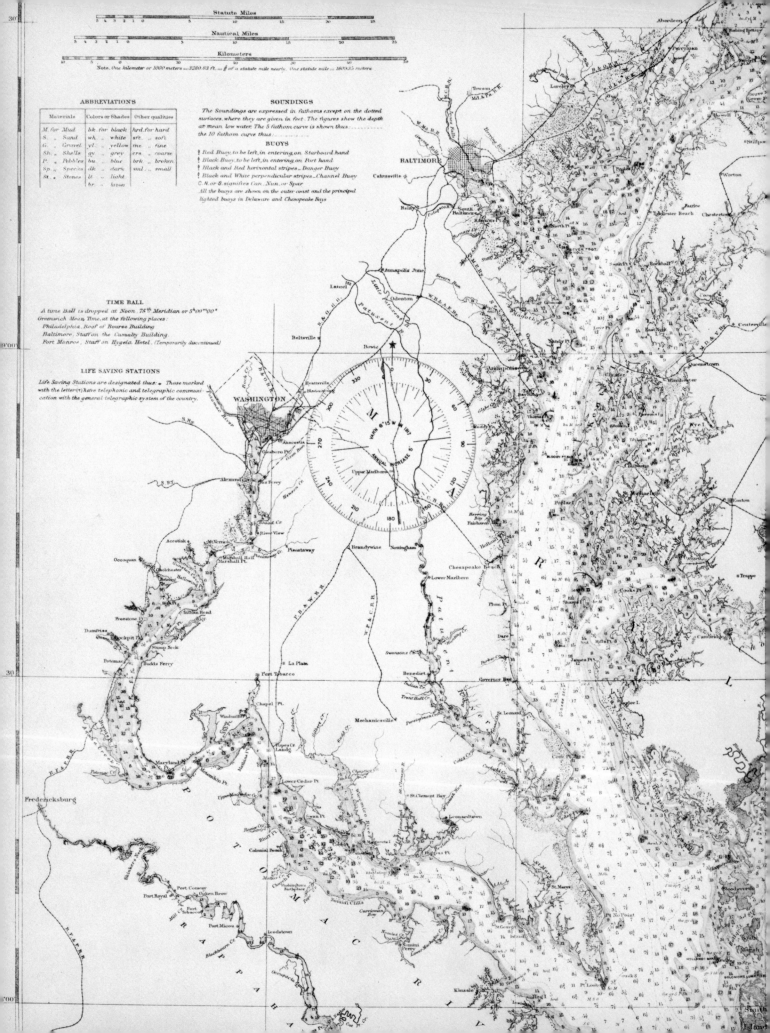

# LVIII

# Potomac River and Chesapeake Bay

## US Coast and Geodetic Survey No 376

*1915*

## 1 : 400,000

*Detail from* DELAWARE AND CHESAPEAKE BAYS. WASHINGTON D.C. COAST AND GEODETIC SURVEY JULY 1915. *Coloured chart, lithograph on paper, 915 × 697 mm. Gnomonic projection.*

This chart has been chosen because it demonstrates how technically superior US charts were to contemporary European charts, perhaps because of the competition promoted by the unusual system of having two hydrographic agencies—the US Coast and Geodetic Survey under the Department of Commerce, and the US Hydrographic Office (renamed US Oceanographic Office in 1962) under the Department of the Navy.

Though produced as long ago as World War I, the clarity of this chart was remarkable, as were the many features not adopted by European hydrographic offices until many years later, such as extensive use of colour printing to emphasise land and shoal water, very careful selection of soundings to prevent overcrowding, much land detail including railroads and rivers, scales in kilometres as well as statute and nautical miles, orange light flares, very clear compass roses, very careful triangulation—all for as little as 50 cents.

The use of standardised conventional signs and abbreviations has always been an important feature of US charts. This conformed fairly closely to British practice, with the important exception of the US method of showing lights and buoys, best seen here at top right, near Annapolis. Note the method of showing the arcs of the red sectors of the lights off Sandy Point and Thomas Point.

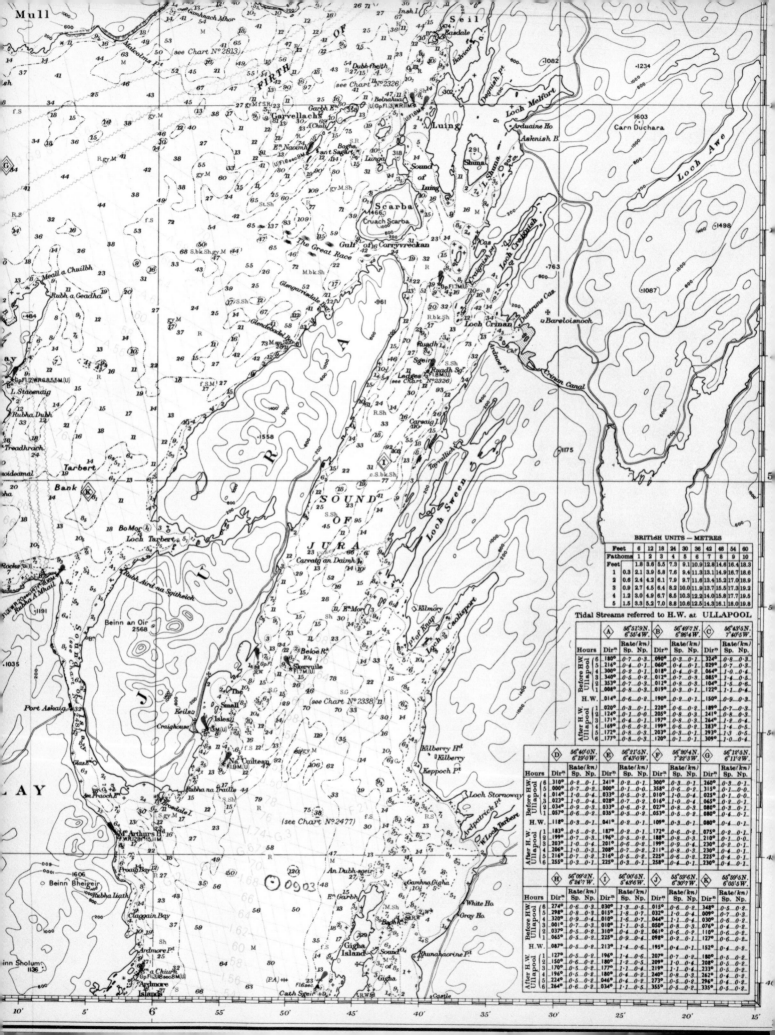

# LIX

## Sound of Jura, Scotland, West Coast

### British Admiralty No L(D3) 2722

*1969*

### 1 : 200,000 (58° 30′N)

*Detail from* ISLAY TO ARDNAMURCHAN POINT FROM BRITISH ADMIRALTY SURVEYS 1904–1967. PUBLISHED—TAUNTON 25TH JULY 1969 UNDER THE SUPERINTENDENCE OF REAR ADMIRAL G. S. RITCHIE, C.B., D.S.C., HYDROGRAPHER OF THE NAVY. (DECCA CHART 25TH JULY, 1969.) *Coloured chart, zinc litho plate from engraved copper original, 680 × 990 mm. Mercator's projection.*

This easy-to-read chart is a result of the chart modernisation scheme put in hand after World War II by Vice-Admiral Sir Guy Wyatt, British Hydrographer of the Navy from 1945 to 1950. Compared with previous British charts, the most striking innovation was the use of colour—a grey tint on the land instead of engraved stipple, and blue for shallow water, in this case in depths under 10 fathoms. Full shading has been displaced by hill contours (now available in most coastal parts of the world), a thickened coastline reflects the use of radar in coastline identification and ranging, and soundings are more openly and evenly spaced as there are less areas unsurveyed in coastal waters. Light stars and cable runs are shown in magenta, the latter being inserted as a result of cable-company complaints of damage to cables by fishermen.

Though lithographic drawing began to supersede copper engraving as a method of producing the basic plate for British Admiralty charts between World Wars I and II, the Hydrographic Department still maintains a staff of engravers to correct the many hundred old copper plates in use and they still engrave new charts on copper for photolitho reproduction. (The record for longevity—and proof of the durability of copper plates—was the plan of Nancowry Harbour, Nicobar Islands, engraved for Dalrymple in 1792 and not superseded until 1959.)

The present process for producing new charts from copper-engraved plates—an example is reproduced opposite—is as follows. The reverse image is engraved by hand, the soundings for the most part being stamped in with an engraving machine. The final image on the engraved plate is filled in with black ink by roller and over this is laid a transparent plastic sheet to which the black ink is transferred under pressure. The plastic sheet with the black ink image is then placed in contact with film and a photographic negative made. This negative is then, by contact printing under an arc lamp, transferred to a zinc lithographic printing plate for use on the printing machine.

This copy of Chart 2722 is overprinted with a 'Decca lattice'—that network of coloured lines for use with Decca Navigator, the British low-frequency radio position-fixing system first used in 1944 during the Allied invasion of Normandy. In the areas covered by Decca 'chains'—and these are continually being extended—charts can be bought either with or without the overprinted lattice.

Obtaining a Decca Navigator 'fix' is extremely simple. The display has (a) a switch for selecting the chain covering the area in which the ship is, and (b) three dials—red, green, and purple—which continuously indicate Decca co-ordinates. On the chart the lattice shows the position lines printed in the appropriate colours—in fact they are hyperbolae—corresponding to the various readings on the dials. To take a fix, the navigator merely reads off the co-ordinates shown on two out of the three dials (the chart tells him which two to read), then, where the position lines corresponding to these co-ordinates intersect on the chart, there is the Decca 'fix'.

For example, the ship is in the southern approaches to the Sound of Jura and the Decca set is switched to the North British chain. If the co-ordinates on the display were Red = G4.6 and Purple = I68.8, then the ship's position would be as indicated opposite by the small circle marked 0903.

# NORTH ATLANTIC OCEAN

# ENGLISH CHANNEL
## TO THE
# STRAIT OF GIBRALTAR
## AND THE
# ARQUIPÉLAGO DOS AÇÔRES

1:3,500,000 (22°30')

DEPTHS IN METRES
HEIGHTS IN METRES

Mercator projection

From the latest information in the Hydrographic Department 1971

Magnetic Variation Curves are for 1970

The annual change in Magnetic Variation is shown at certain positions on the curves. A positive (+) prefix denotes an annual increase, and a negative (−) prefix an annual decrease in the Variation.

**BOUNDARIES.** The International Boundaries shown on this chart are approximate only.

**DOUBTFUL DATA.** Reported but unconfirmed depths or dangers are indicated by an encircling dotted line.

**CABLES.** Only transoceanic cables are shown on this chart.

BAY OF BISCAY

ENGLISH CHANNEL

FRANCE

ESPAÑA
SPAIN

PORTUGAL

IBERIAN BASIN

PORTUGAL CURRENT

Cabo de São Vicente

LISBOA

GIBRALTAR
STRAIT OF GIBRALTAR
MEDITERRANEAN SEA

MAROC
MOROCCO

# LX

# English Channel to the Strait of Gibraltar

**British Admiralty No 24**

*1971*

1 : 3,500,000 (22° 30′N)

*Eastern half of* ENGLISH CHANNEL TO THE STRAIT OF GIBRALTAR AND THE ARQUIPÉLAGO DOS AÇÔRES. PUBLISHED TAUNTON 19TH FEBRUARY, 1971, UNDER THE SUPERINTENDENCE OF REAR ADMIRAL G. P. D. HALL, D.S.C., R.N., HYDROGRAPHER OF THE NAVY. *Colour-printed lithograph on paper, 980 × 630 mm. Mercator's projection*

---

At the present time the area shown opposite is covered by at least eight charts of at least eight different nations, all on much the same scale, and the same applies to many other ocean and coastal areas all over the world. It is this colossal waste of compilation effort that has provided the incentive for the development of the International Chart described in the Introduction (p.13).

The main interest of this final illustration is that it shows part of a chart drawn up and printed according to the specifications now being formulated for the International Chart by the International Hydrographic Organisation in Monaco.

The chart here is British but, in fact, it will eventually be superseded by the appropriate chart in the International $1/3\frac{1}{2}$ m series, to be prepared by France. About a dozen 'member' states of the International Hydrographic Organisation will be adapting the various charts in two International Chart Schemes covering the world on scales of 1/10 million and $1/3\frac{1}{2}$ million.

Of all the innovations on this chart, undoubtedly the most far-reaching for British navigators is that soundings and heights are in metres instead of fathoms and feet—a policy recently adopted by the United Kingdom, Canada, India, South Africa, New Zealand, and Australia for all charts, and by the United States for certain overseas charts.

Other changes that will be noticed compared with, say, Chart LIX, are the solid depth contours instead of the old pecked or dotted fathom lines; the use of a sans serif typeface, none of the lettering being by hand; extensive use of the local language for placenames, sometimes with English translations, eg España, Spain; the use of buff and blue tints for land and shallow water respectively; and the use of magenta for compass roses, cable runs, lines of equal magnetic variation, and for many of the legends.

This metrication policy applies not only to International Charts but also to the new British medium-scale metric charts published since 1968. These are similar in nearly every respect to the small-scale chart described here. However, with over 3,500 charts to be replaced, it will, of course, be many years before the last fathoms-and-feet chart is withdrawn from service.

The four colours used are black, buff, magenta, and blue. By overprinting the buff on the blue, we get a fifth colour, green, used for areas uncovered at low water (there are none shown on this small-scale chart).

This chart has been both drawn and printed lithographically, the basic plate for the black detail being a white enamel-surfaced metal sheet, and those for the magenta, buff and blue details being transparent plastic sheets. In the complicated process needed to produce the basic plate, the fullest use is made of automation and mechanisation—of typeset placenames, soundings and titles; of automatic scribing of chart borders, meridians, parallels, cable runs, etc; and of photography for the transfer of detail from one plate to another.

For printing the final chart, the details on the basic plates for each of the four colours are transferred on to four aluminium printing plates, which are used to produce the charts on a modern four-colour printing machine.

## Bibliography

Ritchie, G. S. 'International Co-operation in Hydrography', *The Journal of Navigation*, XXV, No 1 (January 1972), 2–12

# Acknowledgements

This book could never have been written without the help and
advice of our colleagues in the National Maritime Museum but
it is not possible to mention all of them by name. However, our
especial thanks go to Commander D. W. Waters, Keeper of the
Museum and Head of the Department of Navigation, for reading
through the manuscript in its various stages and for giving us the
benefit of his profound knowledge; and to Mr Barrie Cash who
took many of the photographs.

Rear-Admiral G. S. Ritchie not only contributed the historical
introduction but also helped to select the charts and commented
on the text.

We are particularly grateful to the eminent Dr I. C. Koeman
of Utrecht and Monsieur Marcel Destombes of Paris for giving
so much of their time to read substantial portions of the manuscript; and to Miss Kate Shaw for her Latin and Italian
translations.

Among the many people who helped in special ways, we
would like to thank Professor T. R. Smith of the University of
Kansas; Mrs Marion Brown of Blackheath; Mr W. M.
Whitehill of the Boston Athenaeum; Mr W. T. Wilson of
Messrs. Imray, Laurie, Norie and Wilson Limited; Mrs Virginia
Rust of the Henry E. Huntington Library and Art Gallery, San
Marino, California; Mr R. H. Becker, Bancroft Library,
University of California; Dr Helen Wallis, Mrs Sarah Tyacke,
Mr Hugh Cobbe and Mr John Huddy of the British Museum
Map Room, and the Directors of the Biblioteca Nazionale
Centrale, Firenze and the Biblioteca Nazionale Marciana,
Venezia.

Finally, we are most grateful to the Director, Basil Greenhill,
and Trustees of the National Maritime Museum for their great
encouragement and for their permission to publish this work.

# National Maritime Museum Chart References

| | |
|---|---|
| I | MS 9918/P.13, f.2 |
| II | G.230:1/7 MS, late Portulan 20 |
| III | 38 MS 9920/P.21, f. 11r. and SON/002 |
| IV | 47 MS 9928/P.27, f.1 |
| V | G.201: 1/15 MS, late Portulan 12 |
| VI | G.213: 2/4 MS, late Portulan 2 |
| VII | VAV./001 |
| VIII | NA.G96/36-311C |
| IX | 39 MS 9921/P.12, f.4 |
| X | 36 MS 8924/P.14, f.14r |
| XI | NA69-2N/G.230: 1/21 |
| XII | 51-4/G.215: 1/5 MS, late Portulan 43 |
| XIII | WA/005, f.7 |
| XIV | WA/003, f.13 |
| XV | 39 MS 9931/P.22, f.2 |
| XVI | 47-197/G.224: 1/2 MS, late Portulan 11 |
| XVII | BL/010, f.1 |
| XVIII | 36 MS 9930/P.5, f.6 |
| XIX | G.230: 1/15 MS, late Portulan 41 |
| XX | DUD/002 |
| XXI | CO/3, f.22 |
| XXII | G.246: 2/6 MS |
| XXIII | DO/1, f.19 |
| XXIV | GO/1, f.41 |
| XXV | SEL/014.10, f.3 |
| XXVI | SEL/001 |
| XXVII | 46-181/G.213: 2/2 MS |
| XXVIII | VK/001, f.126 |
| XXIX | 39 MS 9944/P.32, ff.2 and 3 |
| XXX | THO/1, f.39 |
| XXXI | COL/1, f.26 |
| XXXII | JAI/001, f.27 |
| XXXIII | M & P/001, f.8 |
| XXXIV | RUS/1, f.23 |
| XXXV | VK/008, f.37 |
| XXXVI | HER/1, f.26 |
| XXXVII | G.246: 8/2 MS, lent by the Admiralty, 1946 |
| XXXVIII | ROU/001/C, f.1 |
| XXXIX | BEL/001 |
| XL | SPR/1, f.1 |
| XLI | DAL/002, f.37 |
| XLII | 0-033.1, f.28 |
| XLIII | BEL/002a, f.23 |
| XLIV | APR/002, f.42 |
| XLV | MM/003, f.33 |
| XLVI | 31 MS 9938/P.18, plate 6 |
| XLVII | Stevens No. 73 |
| XLVIII | G.246: 3/4 (Boston) MS |
| XLIX | TOF/1, f.25 |
| L | MS 60/017/FLI. 15 |
| LI | G.235: 15/1 (Alexandria) |
| LII | HUR/002, f.30 |
| LIII | SMY/1, f.19 |
| LIV | HN/003, f.103 |
| LV | G.213: 2/14 (1) |
| LVI | G.279: 4/1 (2) |
| LVII | G.285: 2/2, lent by Hydrographer, A.7731, Shelf Rv |
| LVIII | G.246: 2/34, lent by Hydrographer, A.5778, Shelf Rr |
| LIX | G.220: 4/13 (2) |
| LX | G.215: 1/19 |

# Index

Main entries are in **Bold**

Aboukir B, 107
Abrolhos, Houtman's (Western Australia), 61
Acapulco, 73
Admiralty, *see* British Admiralty
Admiralty Chart Committee, 113, 119
Admiralty charts, *see* Charts, nautical
Admiralty Notices to Mariners, 123
Adriatic Sea, **29**
*Adventure*, HMS, 121
Aegean Sea, 29, 45
*Agamemnon*, 125
Agnese, Battista, **33**
Alaska, 129
Albania, 17
Albemarle Sd, **59**
Albert I of Monaco, 13
*Alceste*, frigate, 117
Alderney, 81
Alexander VI, Pope, 27
Alexandria, 9, 91, **117**
Aljubarrota, Battle of, 10
Almagià, Roberto, 21, 23, 29
Altitude of Pole Star, 35, 47
— of Sun, 47
American Independence, War of, 107, 111
Amherst, Colonel, expedition to Newfound-
    land, 109
Amoy, **85**
Amphipolis, Corfu, 17
Amphitrite Is, 87
Amsterdam, 49, 57, 61, 63, 71, 79, 85
Anatolia, 45
Anchorages on charts, 41, 43
Angra, Azores, 71
Anian, Str, 25, 63, 73
Annapolis, 131
Año Nuevo, Pta, 73
Anson, Cdre George, 107
Antarctic, 51
Antonisz, Cornelis, 11
Anticosti I, 35
Antilles, 23, 25
Antwerp, 11, 31
Apian, Peter, 31
Après de Mannevillette, Jean-Baptiste d'
    (1707-30), 101
— atlas *Le Neptune Oriental* (1745), 87, **103**
— chart by (1775), **103**
— atlas *Le Supplement au Neptune Oriental*
    (1781), 103

Aragon, 10, 19
*Arcano del Mare*, by Robert Dudley (1646-7),
    31, **55**
Archangel, 39
Arctic Coasts, 129
Arenas, Pta, 25
Aristotle, 9
Arnold, J. I., 41
Ascension I, 125
Ashley, Sir Anthony, 43, **69**
*Assistant*, HMS, 115
Astrolabe, mariner's, 63
Astronomer Royal, 81
Atkinson, James, 75
Atkinson, Thomas, 91
Atlantic Ocean, 27, **125**
— NE, 19, **135**
— SW, **51**
*Atlantic Neptune, The*, by DesBarres (1784),
    12, **109**, 129
*Atlas of Werelts Water deel... zeecusten...*
    (1663) by the Coloms, 57
*Atlas Maritimus*, by Seller (1675), **67**, 75
*Atlas Maritimus*, by Thornton (1685), **67**, 75
*Atlas Maritimus Novus* (1702-8), **67**, 81
Atlas mountains, 19
*Atlas Nouveau*, by Jaillot (1681), 79
*Atlas François*, by Jaillot (1695), 79
*Atlas Maritimo de España*, by Tofiño (1789),
    **113**
*Atlas...*, by Nagaev (1794), 83
Atlas, sea
— earliest printed, 41
— early English, 11, 43, 55, 65
Australia, 12, 25, 33, 61, 115
Avignon, 19
Azores Is, **71**

Bagrow, Leo, 29
Bahia, 51
Balboa, Vasco N., 33
Baltic Sea, 19, 39, **83**
Ballestir, Joaquin, engraver, 113
Barcelona, 10, 19
Barré, Capt, 117
Barrow, Point, 129
Bar-scales, 53, 67, 69, 101, 131
Bassein estuary, 75
Batavia, *see* Djakarta
Bates paper, 109
Batts, Capt Nathaniel, 59
*Beagle*, HMS, 127
*Bear*, ship, 55
Beaufort, Adml Sir F., 13, 123, 125
Beautemps-Beaupré, 101
Beechey, Capt F. W., 129
Belle Isle Str, 25, 27, 35
Belcher, Capt, 129
Bellin, Jacques Nicholas (1703-72)
— atlas *Le Neptune François* (1753), 12, 93,
    **101**
— atlas *Hydrographie François* (1756-65),
    93
— atlas *Le Petit Atlas Maritime* (1764), 12,
    **93**
— chart of Gibraltar Bay (1765), **93**

Berey, C., engraver, 79
Berey, Nicolas, map colourist, 79
Bermuda, 119
Berry, 129
Bertran, Jaime, 13, 19
Biscay, B of, **47**
Black Sea, 21, 27, **45**
Blackwall, 125
Blackwall frigates, 125
Blaeu, House of, 49
Blaeu, Willem Janszoon (1571-1638), 11, 14,
    **49**
Blachford, publishers, 127
Bligh, William, 115
*Blossom*, HMS, 129
Blue-back charts, 127
Board of Longitude, *see* Longitude
Boards, hinged oak, 53, 69
Boca tigris, 97
Bodega B, 73
Bojador, C, 27
Bombay, 75
Bordone, B., 17, 21
Borneo, 33
Borough, John à, 39
Borough, Stephen, 39
Borough, William, 39, 43, 53
Boschini, M., 17
Boston, Mass, 111
Bottom, nature of, 105, 113, 121
Boufouloc rock, 119
*Bounty*, HMS, 115
Bourne, William, 47
*Braccio*, 107
Bramble shoal, 81
*Brasse*, 13, 33, 93, 107
*Braza*, 13, 33, 107
Brazil, 10, 27, 45
Brazil current, 125
Breadfruit, 115
Brest, Brittany, the Four Passage, 119
British Admiralty, 11, 13, 77, 97, 105, 117, 119,
    121, 125, 133, 135
*British and Irish Coasting Pilot, The Complete
    ... by Heather & Norie* (1835), 123
British manuscript charts, 39, 47, 53, 59, 69,
    73, 89, 111, 115
British Museum, 23, 39, 51
British printed charts, 43, 65, 67, 75, 77, 81,
    87, 95, 97, 99, 105, 109, 117, 119, 121,
    123, 125, 127, 133, 135
Brittany, 41, 101, 119
Brooklyn, 25
Broughton, Capt W, 12
Bruyes, Adml, 117
Buccaneers, 73
Buondelmonte, Cristoforo, 17, 21
Buoys and beacons on charts, 43, 83, 131
Burston, John, 53, 59, 75

Cable runs on charts, 133, 135
Cabot, John, 23, 31
Cabot, Sebastian, 39, 53
Cabot Str, 25
Cabral, Pedro A., 10, 11, 23
Cabrillo, J. R., 33

Cadiz, 113
— Drake's raid on (1587), 39
— Essex's raid on (1596), 55
Caird, Sir James, 14
Cairo, 19, 27
Calicut, 23, 27
California, 33, 73
— as an island, 33, 63, 73
— G of, 33
Callao, 107, 127
Cambridge, Trinity College, 47
Canada, Public Archives of, 89
Canary Is, 9, 11, 101
Canton, 9, 87, 97
— approaches, 97
Cape Breton I, 25, 35
Cape Verde Is, 27
Cape York Peninsula, 61
Caribbean Sea, 107
Carolinas, the, 59, 67
Carpentaria, G of, 61
Carstensz' voyage, with Colster (1623), 61
Cartagena, 107
Carte Pisane, 19
Cartier, Jacques, 27, 35
Casa de Contratacion, 10
Casa da India, 10
Caspian Sea, 21
Casquet rocks, 81
Cassini, Jean, 12
Castille, 10
Catalan charts, 10, 13, 19, 45
Catalonia, 19
Catharine of Braganza, 75
Cathay, 23, 25, 35
Cavendish, Thomas, 55
Centaur, HMS, 117
Central America, 33
Ceylon, 9, 33
Chaleur, B de, 35
Challenger, HMS, 125
Chancellor, Richard, 39, 43
Charles II of England, 12, 53, 59, 65, 67, 73, 75
Charles V, Emperor, 31
Charts, nautical, see also by countries
— British Admiralty, 13, 31
— earliest known, 9, 17, 19
— earliest printed, 21, 29, 37
— earliest printed in English, 43
— early English, 39, 53
— Mercator, see Mercator charts
— plane, see plane charts
— portulan, see portulan charts
Chesapeake B, 131
Chile, 107
Chiloe I, 107
China
— coast near Canton and Hong Kong. Pedro
Blanco and the Mizen, Dalrymple's chart
of the coast of, 97
China Sea, South, 87
Chronometer, marine, 12, 99
Clerk, James, 67, 75
Coastlines on charts, 27, 49
Cobija, 107
Cocchini, Giuseppe, 55

Cod, C, 25, 67
Colbert, J. B., 12, 79
Collins, Captain Greenvile, see Greenvile
Collins
Collins, Freeman, 77
Collinson, 129
Colom, Arnold, 57
Colom, Jacob Aertz
— atlas De Vyenghe Colom (1632, 1636), 57
— atlas The Fierie Sea-Columne (1633–72),
57
— atlas Atlas of Werelts-Water-Deel (1663),
57
Colorado R, 33
Colouring, hand, on charts, 63
Colour printing, 13, 129, 131, 133, 135
Colson, James, 75
Colster's voyage, with Carstensz (1623), 61
Columbus, Christopher, 10, 11, 23
Colvill, Rear Adml Lord, 89
Comberford, Nicholas, 53, 59, 67, 69
Compass, magnetic, 9, 33, 115; see also Mag-
netic variation
Compass rose, 19, 21, 39, 47, 69, 117, 131, 135
— cap of liberty on, 101
Constantinople, 10, 19, 27, 29
Contarini, Giovanni Matteo, 23
Conventional signs and symbols, 12, 43, 108,
137
Cook, James, 12, 25, 31, 51, 63, 89, 97, 99, 115,
129
Copper-engraving, 11, 29, 37, 129, 133
Corfu, 17
Cornwallis, Adml, 119
Correction of charts, 103, 123
Cortereal brothers, 11, 23, 27
Cost of charts, 101, 131
Courageuse, La, 117
Cresques, Jafuda, 10
Crete, 17, 21
Cross-staff, 63
Cuddalore, schooner, 97
Cyprus, 21

Da Gama, Vasco, 10, 11, 23, 27
Dalrymple, Alexander, 12, 13, 91, 97, 103
— Collection of plans and ports in the East
Indies . . . (1774), 97
Daniell, John, 53, 59
Darby, John, 67
Darwin, Charles, 127
Dassigny, Phillipe, 73
Dauphine, le, 25
Da Vinci, Leonardo, 21
Davis, John, 55
de Bry, Theodore, 43
Decca navigator, 133
de Chazelles, 79
Declination, solar, 10, 35
Decoration on charts, 39, 53, 59, 107
de Gennes, 79
de la Favolière, 79
De-la-Haye, G., engraver, 103
de la Voye, 79, 101
Delaware B, 25
de Marre, Jan, 85

D'Entrecasteaux, 13
Dépôt des Cartes et Plans de la Marine, see
Hydrographic Service (French)
Dépôt de la Marine, 101
Depth, Units of, 13, 33, 83, 93, 107, 117, 135
DesBarres, Joseph Frederick Wallet (1721–
1824), 109, 119
— The Atlantic Neptune (1784), 12, 109, 111,
129
— chart of Sable I, Nova Scotia, 109
de Surville, Luis, 107, 127
Dias, Bartolemeu, 10, 27
Dieppe, 25
Dirck Hartog's Ree, 61
Distance, units of, 10, 31, 101, 107
Dividers, 63
Djakarta, 61
Dodecanese Is, 21
Doetecum, Johannes à, 41, 43
Doncker, Hendrick: atlas De Zee-atlas ofte
Water-Waereld . . . (1661), 61, 63, 73
Dover, 49, 65
Dover Castle, 125
Drapers' Company, 53, 75
Drake, Sir Francis, 25, 39, 55
Drake's B, 73
Drake's Estero, 73
Drake's Nova Albion (NW America), 55
Dublin, Trinity College, 39
Duchon, 79
Duckworth, Adml Sir J., 117
Dudley, Sir Robert, atlas Dell'Arcano del
Mare (1646–7), 31, 55
Duff, Vice Adml Robert, 111
Duisburg, 31
Dunn, Samuel, 87
Dutch Charts, see Netherlands Charts
Dutch East India Company, 61

Earwig, ship, 55
East India Company, 12, 75, 117
East Indiamen, 63, 97, 125
East Indies, 61, 97
Ecuador, 73, 107
Edelsland, 61
Edwards, Capt Edward, 115
Elizabeth I of England, 39
Elizabeth of Russia, 83
Elson, T., 129
Embellishment of charts, see Decoration
Endeavour HMS, bark, 99, 115
England
— east coast, 65
— south coast, 49
English Channel, 47, 81, 119, 125
English Pilot, The : by John Seller and others,
1st & 2nd books (1671–2), 11, 65, 67, 77,
81, 127
English charts, see British Charts
Engraved charts, see charts, nautical; copper-
engraving; woodcuts
Enkhuizen, 41
Eratosthenes, 9, 10
Erebus, HMS, 51
Essex's raid on Cadiz, 1596, 55
Establishment of the port, 47, 109

Estonia, 39, 43
Everaerts, Martin, 41

Faden, William, 113
Farallon Is, 73
Fathoms
— English, 93, 117
— French, 93, 117
— Russian, 83
— Spanish, 107
Fayal, Azores, 71
Fear, C, 27
Feet, English, 93
— French, 93
Fer, I de, *see* Hierro
Ferrol, 113
Fez, 19
*Fierie Sea-Columne, The*, atlas by the Coloms, (1633–72), 57
Finland, G of: 39; by Borough, 43; by Nagaev [1750], 83
Fisher, James, 75
FitzRoy, Capt R., 127
Fix, navigational, 47, 91, 133
Flags on charts, 19, 27
Flamsteed, John, 81
Flemish Is, *see* the Azores
Flinders, Matthew, 12, **115**
Flinders' bar, 115
Florence, 11, 23, 25, 27, 33, 45, 55
— Bibl Med Laurenziana, 17
— Bibl Nazionale Cent, 23
Flores, 25
Florida, 25
Forlani, Paolo, 29, 37
Fortunate Is, *see* Canary Is
Four Passage, Brest, 119
Fox, George, 59
France, SW, **79**
Francis I of France, 25, 35
Franklin, Capt John, 129
French charts, 91, 93, 101, 103
French revolution, 101
Frisius, Gemma, 31
Fukien, China, 85

Galilei, Galileo, 12
Gascony, 79
Gascoyne, Joel, 59, 71, 75
Genoa, 9, 19, 25
Georgia, 69
*Geographia*, by Claudius Ptolemy, 9, 10–11, 14
Gernez, D., 41
Gibraltar, 91, 93, 111
Gibraltar B, by Bellin [1764], **93**
Gibraltar Str, 91
Gilollo, 33
Giovo, Giulio, 25
Gironde estuary: by Jaillot [1693], 79
Globes, 31
Goa, 27
Gogland I (Götland), 83
Golden Gate, 73
Good Hope, C of, 10, 23, 27, 125
Goos, Abraham, 63
Goos, Hendrik, 63

Goos, Pieter, 63, 67
— *Zee Atlas* (1666), **63**, 67
Götland, 39, 83
Graham, Reginald, 75
Granada, 19
Grand Turk, 45
Great Sole Bank, 47
Great Southern Continent, 11, 12, 31, 51, 97, 99
Greek Archipelago, 17, 21, 29
Green, Charles, 99
Green, Messrs R. & H., 125
Greenvile Collins, Capt, 11–12, 65, 69, 77
Greenvile Collins, Capt, chart of the Scilly Is (1689), **77**
Greenvile Collins, Capt, *Great Britain's Coasting Pilot* (1693), 69, **77**
Greenwich meridian, 101, 109, 129
— Royal Observatory, 12, 65, 81, 109
Guadgnino, *see* Vavassore
Guienne, 79
Guipuzcoa, 79
Gulf Stream, 125

Hachuring, curved, 93
Hack, William, 73
Hadley quadrant, 12
Hague, the, Royal Library, 51
Hakluyt, Richard, 25
Halifax, NS, 89, 109
Hall, Rear Adml G. P. D., 135
Halley, Edmond (1656–1742), 125
— chart of the English Channel, 81
Halmahara, 33
Harbours on charts, 49
Harrison, John, 12
Hartog, Dirck, voyage (1616), 61
Harvard University, 111
Hassler, F. R., 13
Hatfield House, 39
Hatteras, C, 25, 67
Hawkesworth, J., *Account of the Voyages . . . Southern Hemisphere* (1773), 99
Hayward, Lt, 115
Heather, William (*fl* 1740–1812), 123, 127
Heather & Norie's: *The Complete British and Irish Coasting Pilot . . .* [1833], **123**
— chart of the Solent . . . (1833), **125**
Hebrides, 105
*Hector*, HMS, 111
Helsinki, 39
Henry IV of England, 27
Henry the Navigator, Prince, 10, 19, 27
Herbert, William (1718–95)
— *A New Directory for the East Indies* (1758), 87
— chart of the South China Sea (c 1758), 87
Hierro, 101
High Water Full and Change, *see* Establishment of the Port
Hillegom, voyage of Van (1618), 61
Hojeda, 23
Holland, Samuel, 119
*Hollandia Nova, see* Australia
Homem, Diogo, 29, **37**
Homem, Lopo, 37

Hondius, Jodocus, 43
Hong Kong, 97
Hood, Thomas, 47, 53
Horn, C, 25, 51, 73
Houtman's Abrolhos, 61
Houtman's voyage (1619), 61
Howard, Lord, 11
Hudson R, 25
Hundred Years' War, 17
Hurd, Capt Thomas (1757–1823), 13
— *Charts of the English Channel . . .* (1811), 119
— chart of the approaches to Brest (1807), 119
Hydrographer of the Navy, 12–13, 97, 117, 119, 133
Hydrographer to the East India Company, 12, 75, 97, 117
Hydrographic Department/Office (British), 12, 117, 119
— US, *see* US Hydrographic Office
Hydrographic Service (French), 12, 59, 93, 101, 117
*Hydrographie Française*: atlas by Bellin and others (1756–65), 93

Ice, 83, 129
Icy C, 129
Iezo Str, 55
Imray, James & Son, 127
Imray, Laurie, Norie & Wilson Ltd, 127
Ingermanland, Estonia, 43
International charts, 13, 135
International Hydrographic Organisation Bureau, 13, 135
*Investigator*, HMS, 115
Ionian Is, 21
Isabella of Burgundy, 71
Islands on charts, 27, 53, 115
*Isolaria*, or island-books, 10, 17, 21
Italian maps and charts, 17, 21, 23, 25, 29, 33, 37, 55

Jacomo, Mestre, 19
Jaffa, 117
Jaillot, Alexis Hubert (1632–1712), 79
Jamaica, 95
James II of England, 65, 73, 75
Jansson (Janssonius), Jan, 49
Japan, 10, 33
Java, 33
Jeffreys, Thomas, 89
Jenkinson, 43
Jerusalem, 19, 27
João I of Portugal, 10, 27
João III of Portugal, 27
John of Gaunt, 10
Johnson, John, *see* Jansson, Jan
Johnson, William, *see* Blaeu, W. J.
Juan Fernandez Is, 107
Jupiter's satellites, 12
Jura, Sd of, 133

Keats, John, 33
Kendall, Abraham, 55
Kendall, Larcum, 12

Keulen, Johannes Van, *the elder*, 12
— atlas *The Great . . . Sea Atlas or Water-world*, (1682), 71
— atlas *The New Large Shining Sea-Torch*, 12
— *the younger*, **85**
— chart of the port of Amoy [1753], 85
Keulen, Gerard Van, 71
Keulen, Gerard Hulst Van, 71
Kingston, Jamaica, 95
Kino, Father, 63
Koeman, Dr C., 15, 41
Korea, 33
Kronstadt, 83
Kurile Is, 63

Labrador, 23, 27
Labyadnikov, M., 83
Lackateyn, Amoy, 85
Ladrones Is, 63
Lafreri, Antonio, 11, 37
Landau-Finaly collection, 23
La Perouse, J. F. de G., 13
Latitude scales, 13, 23, 25, 33, 47, 77, 99
Latitude, finding of, 35, 61
Latvia, 43
Laurie, Robert, 127
Leading and clearing lines, 21, 111
Leagues
— Breton, 101
— Catalan, 10
— English, 101
— French, 101
Leeskart, 11
Leghorn, 45, 51
Leicester, Earl of, 55
Le Maire, 61
Leningrad, 39
Levant, 45
Lewis (Outer Hebrides), 105
Leyden, 41
*Licht der Zee-vaert, Het*, atlas by Jansson/ Blaeu, 11, 49
*Lichtende Columne ofte Zeespiegel*, atlas by Doncker (1665), 61
*Lichtende Columne ofte Zeespiegel*, atlas by Pieter Goos (1650), 63
*Light of Navigation, The*, by Blaeu (1620), **49**
Liefland, *see* Lyfland
Lima, 107
*Lion*, ship, 39
Lisbon, 10, 27, 37, 51
Lithography, 13, 37, 129, 133, 135
'Little Midshipman, The', at the sign of, 123
Livonia, 43
Lizard, 101
Logan airport, 111
London, 37, 39, 43, 47, 53, 59, 65, 67, 69, 73, 75, 77, 81, 87, 95, 97, 99, 101, 105, 109, 117, 119, 121, 123, 125, 127
*London*, ship, 97
Longitude
— Board of (English), 12, 81, 119
— finding, 12, 65, 99
— scales, 9, 13, 23, 25, 33, 61, 99, 101, 109

Lopez, Don Diego, 73
Lords Proprietors' map, 69
Louis IX of France (St Louis), 19
Louis XIV of France (le Roi Soleil), 12, 79
Louvain, 31
Lubbock, Basil, 125
Lucini, Antonio Francesco, 55
Lunar distance observations, 12, 99
Lyfland, 39, 43

Macao, 27, 97
Mackenzie, Murdoch Sr (1712–97), 12, **105**, 113
Mackenzie, Murdoch Jr (1743–1829), 12, 105
Mackenzie R, 129
Madeira, 25
Madrid, 113
Magellan, Ferdinand, 10, 25, 33
Magellan Str, 33
Magnetic information on charts, 25, 81, 129, 135
— meridian, 109
— needle, 9
— variation, 17, 39, 81, 125
Majorca, 19, 45
Malta, 21, 45, 121
Manhatten, 25
Maranhão, 51
*Maréchal d'Estrées, le*, 103
*Mariner's Mirror, The*, atlas by Waghenaer (1588), 11, 43
Marinus of Tyre, 9
*Maritim Survey of Ireland and the West of Great Britain, A*, by Murdoch Mackenzie Sr (1776), **105**
Marquesas Is, 33
Marre, Jan de, 85
Marseilles, 45, 91
Martellus, H., 17
Martin, Adml Sir W. Fanshawe, 89
Maryland, 67
Matto Grosso, 51
Mauritius, 115
McClure, 129
Mediterranean, 19, 27
— Central, **37**
— East, **29**, 45
— West, **53**, 91
— charts by Roux (1764), **91**
— charts used on board HM Ships *Theseus* (1793) and *Victory* (1807), 91
Melchor, Don, 73
Mendocino, C, 73
Mercator, Gerard, 11, 31
Mercator's projection, 11, 31, 39, 47, 55, 67, 113
Merchant Taylors' School, 47
Mercury B, 99
Meridian, prime, 11, 101, 129
Meridional parts, 31
Messina, 45
— str of, 91
Metric system, 13, 135
Mexico, 33
— G of, **69**, 109

Miles,
— Dutch, 11
— French, 31
— German, 31, 83, 101
— Italian, 31, 83, 101
— nautical, 83, 101, 131
— 'portulan', 10
— statute, 131
— Spanish, 11
Millo, Antonio, 17
Mina, 27
Minches, The, 105
Minet, 79
Mizen, The (South China Coast), 97
Mocenigo, Giovanni, 21
Moluccas Is, 33
Monaco, 13, 135
Montcalm, Gen, 89
Monterey, 73
Montreal, 35
Moore, Jonas, 65
Moore, J. Hamilton, 127
Morlaix, Brittany, 41, 101
Mortier, Pierre, **79**
Moscow, 83
Mount & Page, 67, 81, 127
Moxon, Joseph, *Book of Sea Plats* (1657), 65
Muscovy Company, 39
Murari, Giacomo, 37

Nagaev, Capt Alexei, 83
Nancowry Harb, 123
Naples, 45
Napoleon I of France, 111
Narbrough's chart of the South Seas (1673), 75
— voyage (1669–71), 77
Narva, 39
National Maritime Museum, 12, 14, 39, 69, 89, 117, 136
— catalogue of the Library, volume III: Atlases and cartography, 15
*Nautical Almanac, The*, 99, 101, 109
*Nautical Magazine, The*, 123
Naze of Norway, 39
Needles, The, 123
Nelson, Lord, 91, 117
*Neptune Français* (1800–24), 101, 119
*Neptune François, Le* [1693], 12, 79
*Neptune François, Le*, atlas by Bellin (1753), 93
*Neptune Oriental, Le*, atlas by d'Après de Mannevillette (1745), 87, **103**
*Neptune Oriental, Supplément au*, atlas by d'Après de Mannevillette (1781), 103
Netherlands charts, 11, 31, 41, 43, 49, 57, 61, 63, 71, 79, 85
New England, 27, 67, 109, 127
Newfoundland, 23, 25, 27, 35, 45, 69
New Guinea, 33, 61, 115
New Holland, *see* Australia
New Jersey, 67
Newport, Maine, 25
New York, 25, 109
— Public Library, 59
New Zealand, 25, 33, 63, **99**
Niccoli, Niccolò, 17

Nicholson, William, 87
Nile, Battle of, 117
Nile, R, 51
Nordenskiöld, A. E., 15, 129
Norie, John William (1772–1843), **123**
— British coasting pilot by, 123
— *Epitome of Practical Navigation* (1805), 123
Norie & Wilson, 127
Norman, Robert, 53
North America, E Coast, 25, 67
— West coast, **55**
*North-American Pilot*, by Sayer & Bennett (1775), 89
North Atlantic drift current, 125
North Carolina, **59**
North-east Trade Winds, 125
North Sea, **39**, 57
*Northumberland*, HMS, 89
Norumbega, 27
Nova Albion, 55
Nova Scotia, 25, 27, 69
— survey by DesBarres, 109
Nunes, Pedro, 10, 11
Nuyts & Thijssen voyage (1626–7), 61
Nuytsland, Australia, 61

Öland, Baltic Sea, 39
Oliva family, 19, 45
— Joan, **45**
— Joannes, 51
*Orcades*, by Murdoch Mackenzie, Sr, 12
Orkney, 105
Orléans, I de, 35, 89
Ortelius, Abraham, 11, 37
Owers shoal, 81

Pacific Ocean, 25, **33**, 63
— South, 31
— NW American coast, 55
Pagano, Matteo, 29
Palawan, 33
Palisades, the (Port Royal, Jamaica), 95
Palermo, 45
Palla-Strozzi, 10
Palma, Canary Is, 25, 43
Palma, Majorca, 10
Pamlico Sd, 25, 59
Panama, 73, 109
*Pandora*, HMS, 115
*Panther*, HMS, 111
Pará, 51
Paracel Is, 87
*Paramore*, pink, 81
Paris, 93, 101, 103, 113
— Bibliothèque Nationale, 19
— Observatoire, 12
Parry, Adml Sir John, 13
Paskart, 11
Paste-on corrections to charts, 103
Payta, 107
Pedro Blanco (South China coast), 97
Pelsaert's voyage (1629), 61
*Pembroke*, HMS, 89
Péne, Charles, 79
Pepys, Samuel, 11, 53, 59, 65, 69, 77

Pernambuco, 51
Perrenot, Nicholás, 31
Persian G, 9
Peru, 33, 107, **127**
Peter the Great of Russia, 83
*Petit Atlas Maritime, Le*, by Bellin (1764), 12, 93
Philippine Is, 33
Photography, 129, 135
Photolithography, *see* Lithography
Pilot books, 17; *see also* sailing directions; portolano
Pierre, L, 35
Pizarro, Francisco, 33
Place names on charts, 19, 25, 27
Plane charts, 31, 47, 53, 67
Planisphere, 23
Plantin, C., 41
Plate, R, 51
'Platt, at the sign of', 53, 69
*Plymouth*, HMS, 77
Pole star, 9, 10, 35
Polo, Marco, 10, 23
Ponta Delgada, Azores, 71
Porcacchi, T., 17
Portland, Dorset, 49
Portlock, Capt, 115
Portobello, 107
*Portolano*, 9, 19
Port Royal harbour, Jamaica: chart by Speer (c 1766), **95**
Portuguese charts, 10, 35, 37, 51
Portulan charts, 9, 19, 53, 67
Position lines, *see* Fix
Potomac R, **129**
Prado, 61, 115
Prinald, engraver, 95
*Prince of Wales*, ship, 125
Printed charts, *see* charts, nautical
Printing, invention of, 11
Projection, *see* Mercator projection; plane charts
*Providence*, HMS, 115
Prunes family, 19
Ptolemy, Claudius, 9–10, 14, 23, 51
Pythagoras, 9

Quadrant, 10
— Hadley, 12
Quebec, 35, 89
Queen Charlotte's Sd, 99

Radar, 133
Radcliffe, London, 53, 59
Raleigh, Sir Walter, 25, 59
Razaut, 79
Red Sea, 9, 19, 33
'Regiment of the North Star', 10, 35
Reinel, Pedro & Jorge, 10, 27
Renaud, Ingénieur Hydrographe, 13
Return Reef, 129
Reval (Tallinn), 39, 43
Reyes, Pt, California, 73
Rhodes, 17, 19, **21**
Rhumb lines, 9, 10, 19, 53, 59
Riczo, Joan, 45

Ringrose, Basil, **73**
Ripol, Berenguer, **19**
Ripraps shoal (Le Colbort), 81
Ritchie, Rear Adml G. S., 133, 136
Roanoke, 59
Roaring forties, 125
Rocks on charts, 21, 37, 41, 43
Rodgers, Commodore, 129
*Romney*, HMS, 89
*Rosario*, 73
Roscoff, Brittany, 41
Ross, James Clark, 51
Ross, Adml J. Lockhart, 111
Rosselli, Francesco, 21, **23**, 25
Rosselli, Lorenzo, Cosimo and Alessandro, 23
Rouille, minister, 101
Roux, Joseph
— charts of the Mediterranean Sea, **91**
— plans of the principal ports and anchorages in the Mediterranean, 91
Royal Astronomical Society, 121
Royal Geographical Society, 121
*Royal George*, HMS, 111
Royal Observatory, *see* Greenwich
Royal Society, 99, 121
Rumania, 45
Rupelmunde, 31
Russia, King of, 45
Russian atlases and charts, 83
Rutlinger, Johannis, 43
Rutters, *see* pilot books
Ryther, Augustine, 43

Sable Is, Nova Scotia, chart by DesBarres (1779), **109**
Sabran, 79
Sagres, 10
Saguenay, R, 35
Saigon, 87
Sailing directions, 17, 41, 65; *see also* Pilot books
St Augustine, 69
St Croix, Peter, 81
St Helena, 111, 125
St John of Jerusalem, Knights of, 17, 21
St Lawrence, R and G, 27, **35**, 89, 109
St Malo, 35, 41
St Petersburg, 39, 83
St Pol, Brittany, 41, 101
St Vincent, Adml Lord, 117
Sale of charts, 119, 127
Sallset, Bombay, **75**
Sanches, Antonio, **51**
Sancti Angeli, Corfu, 17
Sandwich, Lord, 53
San Francisco, 73
Sanson, Guillaume and Adrien, 79
Santander, Spain
— plan of port by Tofiño (1788), **113**
Sant Andreus, C, 73
Santiago di Compostela, 19
Saveur, 79
Sayer & Bennett, 127; *North-American Pilot* (1775), 89
Scales, *see* bar-scales
Scheldt expedition (1808–9), 121

Schiso Pt, Sicily, 121
Schouten & Le Maire: voyage of circum-navigation (1615–17), 61
Scilly Is, 47; chart by Greenvile Collins (1689), 77
Scotland, west coast, 105
Sea chart, see chart, nautical
Sea-monsters on charts, 41, 59
Seller, John (d 1697), 69, 75, 77, 127
— *The English Pilot*, 11, 65
— *Atlas Maritimus*, 67, 75
Sept Is, Les, Brittany, 101
*Seringapatam*, ship, 125
Seven Years' War, 89
Seville, 27
Sextant, 99
*Shannon*, ship, 125
Sharpe, Capt Bartholemew, 73
Shoals on charts, 37, 57
Siberia, 129
Sicily, 10, 19, 121
Skagerrak, the, 39
Skaw, the, 39
Skelton, R. A., 15, 21, 23, 35
Skye, 105
Smith, Capt John, 69
Smith, Prof T. R., 53
Smyth, Adml William Henry
— atlas, *The Hydrography of Sicily, Malta and the adjacent islands . . .* (1823), 121
— plan and views of Taormina, 121
Solent, the, 89
— chart by Heather & Norie (1833), 123
Sonetti, Bartolommeo dalli, 17, 21, 29
Sound, the, 39
Soundings on charts, 53, 73, 83, 131
— deep-sea, 125
— early, 11, 33, 41, 47
South Carolina, 69
Southern Continent, see Great Southern Continent
South Sea Waggoner, 73
Spain, 29
Spanish charts, 107, 113
*Speculum Nauticum*, atlas by Waghenaer (1584), 41
Speed, John, 77
Speer, Capt Joseph
— *The West India Pilot* (1766), 95
Spence, Graeme, 12
*Spieghel der Zeevaerdt*, atlas by Waghenaer (1586), 11, 41, 43
Spithead, 123
Spry, Adml, 109
Square grid, 59, 115
Stadia, 9, 31
Staten I, 25
Station pointer, 72
*Stella maris*, see Pole Star
Stepney, 53
Stevens, Henry Newton, 109
Sumatra, 9
— chart of the West coast, 103
Sunda Str, 61
Sunderland, 125

Surveying service (British), 119
Surville, see de Surville
Syene, 9
*Sylph*, HMS, 111
Syria, 29

Tahiti, 99
Tallinn, Estonia, 39, 43
Taormina, Sicily, 121
Taprobana, 33
Tasman, Abel, 25, 61, 63, 99
Tasmania, 25, 63
Taunton, 133, 135
Taylor, Prof E. G. R., *Haven Finding Art*, 9
Tenerife, 101, 113
Terceira, Azores, 71
Thames estuary, 65
Thames school of plattmakers, 53, 59, 65, 69, 75
*Theatrum Orbis Terrarum*, by Ortelius, 11
*Theseus*, HMS, 91
Thijssen, 61
Thornton, John, 53, 59, 67, 69, 75, 81
Thornton, Samuel, 81
Tidal information on charts, 47, 81; see also Establishment of the Port
Timekeepers, see chronometers
Timor, 33
Timor Sea, 61
Tipa, Macao, 97
Tofiño, Don Vicente
— *Atlas Maritima de España* (1789), 113
— *Cartas Maritimas de la Costa de España* (1788), 113
*Toise*, 93, 101, 107
Tonkin, G of, 87
Tordessillas, Treaty of, 10, 27, 33
Torres, Luis V. de, 61, 115
Torres Str, 61, 115
Toulon, 91, 117
Tower of London, 53
Tracks on charts, 91, 125, 127
Transit of Venus, 99
Traverse, the (St Lawrence R), 89
Triangulation, 12, 105, 131
Tridinensis, G. de P., 21
*Trinity*, the, 73
Trinity House, 39, 77
Troubridge, Adml Sir T., 117
Tsiompa, Cochin-China, 87
*Tuessa*, 107
Turco, Bartolommeo, 21

Ulloa, F. de, 33
US charts, 13, 129, 131
US Coast Survey, 13
US Coast and Geodetic Survey, 13, 129, 131
Ushant, 47
US Hydrographic Office, 13, 129, 131
US Oceanographic Office, 131

Valdivia, 107
Valencia, 70
Vallard, 35
Valletta, 91

Vancouver, George, 12
Van Diemens Land, see Tasmania
Van Hillegom, 61
Van Keulen family, see Keulen, van
Van Loon, H., 79
*Vara*, 107
Vavassore, Giovanni Andreas di (*fl* 1520–72), 29
Vellum manuscript charts, 17, 19, 21, 25, 27, 33, 35, 39, 45, 47, 51, 53, 59, 69
Vellum printed charts, 53
Venice, 9, 17, 19, 21, 23, 27, 29, 33, 37, 45
Verde, C, 27
Vermilion Sea, 33
Verrazana, 25
Verrazano, Girolamo, 25
Verrazano, Giovanni, 25, 59
Verrazano, Sea of, 25, 63
Vespucci, Amerigo, 11, 23
*Victory*, HMS, 91
Vidal, Citizen, 117
— Alexander, T. E., Vice Adml, 111, 117
— E. Essex, 111
— Emeric, 111
— Richard E., 111
*Vidal*, HMS, 111
Views, coastal, 41, 43, 49, 65
Virginia, 59, 67
Vitry, Bishop J. de, 9
Vooght, Claes Jansz, 71
Vries, Maarten, 63
Vyborg, 39, 83
*Vyerighe Colom, Het*, atlas by the Coloms (1632, 1636), 57

'Waggoners', 41, 53, 59, 73
Waghenaer, Lucas Janszoon (1533–1606), 11, 41, 43, 49
Walker, J. & C., engravers, 125
Walvis B, 27
Wapping, London, 53, 73
Washington, DC, 13, 129, 131
Welch, Andrew, 69
*West-India Pilot, The*, by Speer (1766), 95
West Indies, 69
Whampoa, 97
Willoughby, 43
Wilson, see Norie & Wilson
Winds on charts, 9, 19
Wolfe, Gen James, 89
Woodcuts, 11, 21, 29
World, 23
Wright, Edward, 11, 31, 47
Wyatt, Adml Sir Guy, 133

York, Duke of, 53
Yucatanet, 25

Zamberti, Bartolommeo, see Sonetti, B. delli
*Zee-Atlas*, by Doncker (1661), 61, 63, 73
*Zee-Atlas*, by Goos (1666), 63, 67
*Zee-Atlas*, by the Van Keulens (1680), 71
*Zee-Fakkel*, by the Van Keulens (1681–4), 12, 71, 85
*Zee-Spiegel*, by Jansson/Blaeu, 49